Eight a d

A.L.Griffiths

OLIVER & BOYD

Oliver & Boyd
Longman House
Burnt Mill
Harlow
Essex CM20 2JE

An Imprint of Longman Group UK Ltd

ISBN 0 05 003925 3
First published 1987
Fourth impression 1990

Set in 12pt Linotype Melior Roman
Designed and illustrated by Scorpion Pica
Produced by Longman Group (FE) Ltd
Printed in Hong Kong

NUMBER

MONEY

1

Write a numeral for each of these numbers.

1

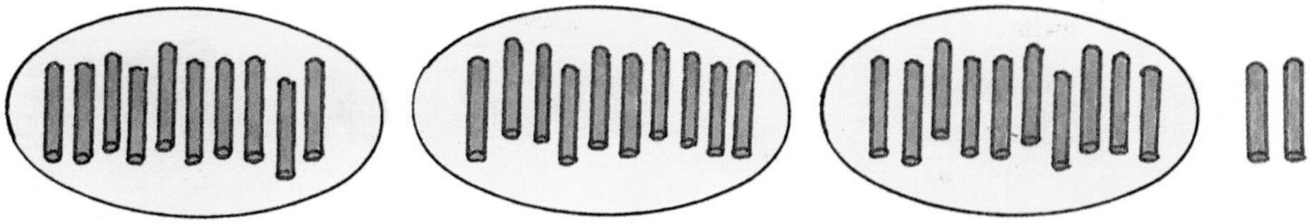

2

3

4

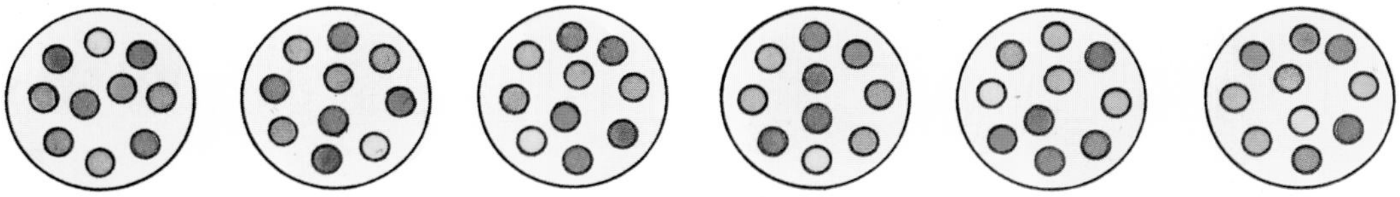

5

6

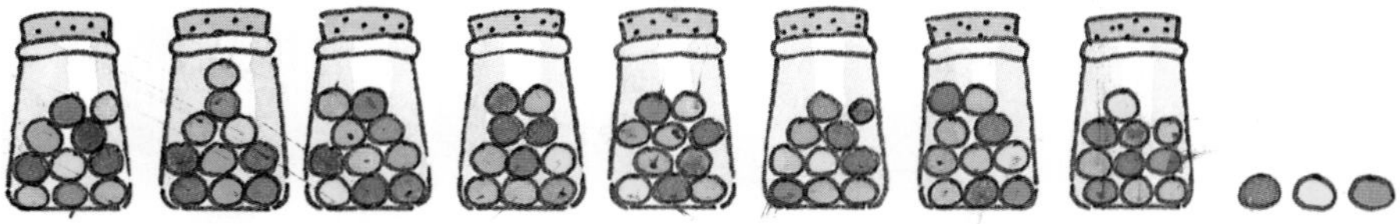

7

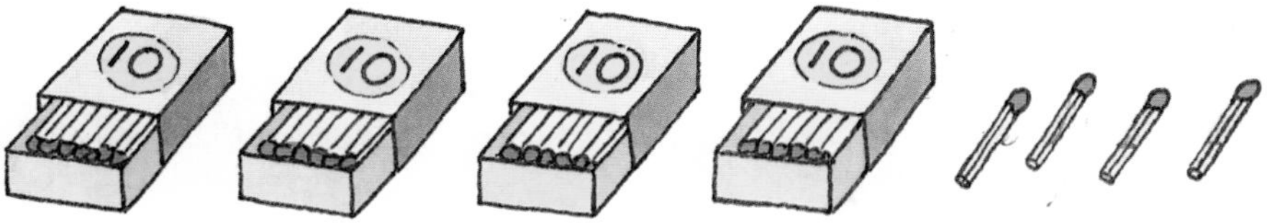

8

2

Write a numeral for each of these numbers.

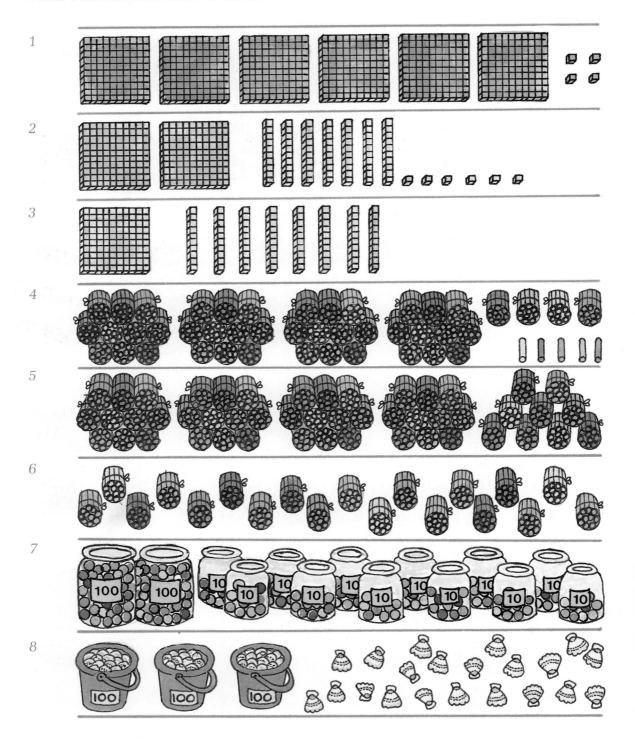

3

How many small cubes are there in each of these pictures?

1

1000 cubes

2

3

4

5

6

7

8

4

This box holds 1000 drawing pins.

This box holds 100 drawing pins.

This box holds 10 drawing pins.

Write in words the number of drawing pins shown in each of the pictures below.

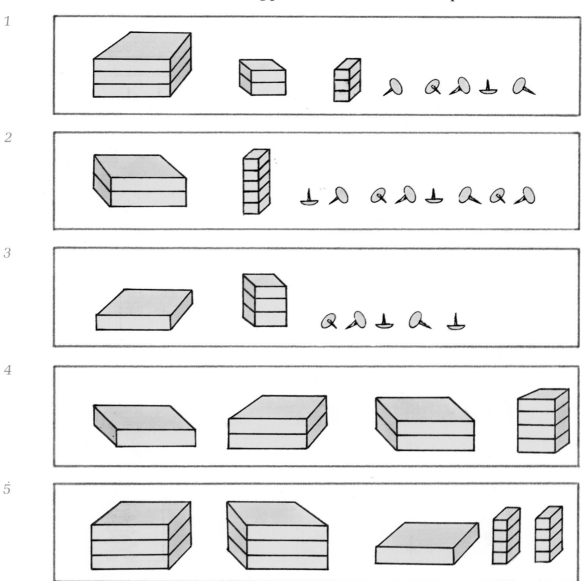

6

7

8

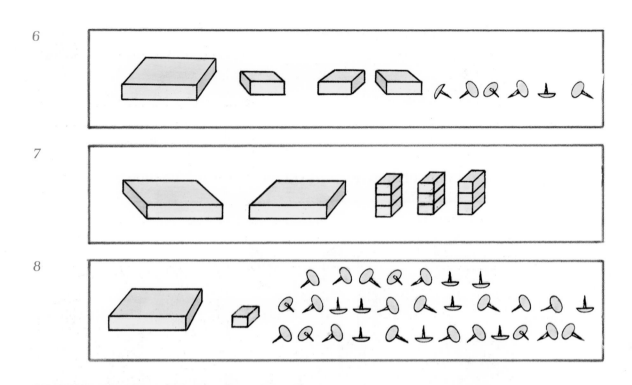

5
Write these abacus numbers in words.

1

2

3

4

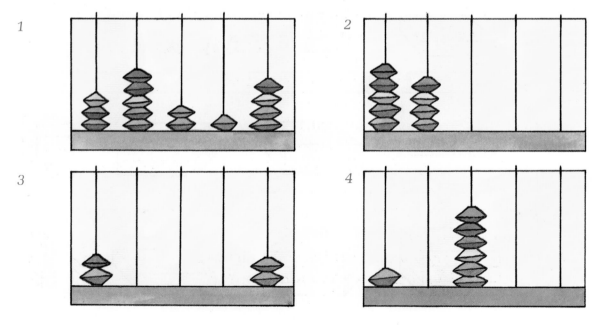

Write these calculator numerals in words.

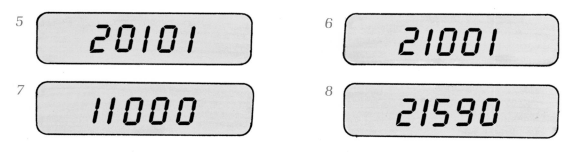

5   20101

6   21001

7   11000

8   21590

6

1 How many chocolate beans are there in this picture?
2 If 2 tins of 100 were taken away, how many chocolate beans would be left?
3 If 7 boxes of 1000 were added to those in the picture,
   how many chocolate beans would there be?
4 If 6 boxes of 10 were added to those in the picture,
   how many chocolate beans would there be then?
5 If 1 tin of 100 and 3 single beans were taken from those in the picture,
   how many chocolate beans would there be then?
6 If 2 tins of 100 and 4 boxes of 10 were taken from those in the picture,
   how many chocolate beans would there be then?
7 If 5 boxes of 10 and 7 single beans were added to those in the picture,
   how many chocolate beans would there be then?
8 If 8 boxes of 1000 were added to those in the picture,
   how many chocolate beans would there be then?

7

Write each of these in digits.

1 twenty thousand two hundred and thirty-seven
2 seventy-seven thousand four hundred and six
3 forty-three thousand nine hundred
4 eighty-five thousand seven hundred and four
5 thirty thousand and twenty-seven
6 ten thousand and nine
7 sixty thousand and eighty
8 twenty thousand nine hundred.

8

Write a numeral for each of these abacus numbers.

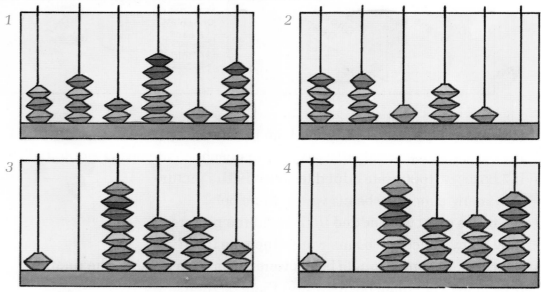

Write these calculator numerals in words.

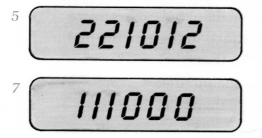

9

Find the next two numbers in each of the lines below.

1 85	*2* 850	*3* 8500	*4* 85 000
90	900	9000	90 000
95	950	9500	95 000
▮	▮	▮	▮
▮	▮	▮	▮

5 70 000	*6* 300 000	*7* 25 000	*8* 60 000
80 000	450 000	50 000	75 000
90 000	600 000	75 000	90 000
▮	▮	▮	▮
▮	▮	▮	▮

10

Write the answers to these in digits.

1 Add one thousand to 362 423.

2 Add thirty thousand to 465 343.

3 Take six hundred thousand from 987 668.

4 Take fifteen thousand from 555 555.

5 Add twenty thousand to 440 600.

6 Take one thousand one hundred from 111 111.

7 Take ten thousand from 111 111.

8 Take one hundred and one thousand from 111 111.

11

Write the answers to these in words.

1 What number is 9 more than 999?

2 What number is 10 less than 10 000?

3 Take 900 from 9000.

4 What number is 100 more than 990?

5 How many less than 7794 is 6784?

6 Find the difference between 85 629 and 89 729.

7 What must be added to 50 450 to make 60 460?

8 What is the difference between 266 400 and 206 400?

12

1 What is the greatest number you can name with the digits 6, 7 and 8?
2 What is the greatest 4-digit number?
3 What is the greatest number you can name using the digits 3,5 and 9?
4 What is the smallest number you can name with the digits 4, 5, 6 and 1?
5 What is the greatest even number you can name with the digits 4, 9, 3 and 8?
6 What is the greatest 4-digit even number?
7 What is the greatest 5-digit even number?
8 What is the smallest 4-digit odd number you can name using the digits 7, 6, 5 and 0?

13

The symbol > in mathematics means **is greater than**.
The symbol < in mathematics means **is less than**.

468 > 437   **4362 < 6432**

means **468 is greater**   means **4362 is less**

than 437.   **than 6432.**

Write >, < or = in place of 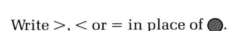.

1   1100 ⬤ 1011
2   3967 ⬤ 4067
3   10 673 ⬤ 10 673
4   6347 ⬤ 6347
5   29 649 ⬤ 29 496
6   47 862 ⬤ 43 999
7 128 000 ⬤ 119 888
8 205 600 ⬤ 211 400

14

Write >, < or = in place of ⬤.

1   9532 ⬤ 9000 + 50 + 30 + 2
2   6749 ⬤ 6000 + 700 + 40 + 0 + 9
3   7603 ⬤ 7000 + 600 + 30
4   8719 ⬤ 8000 + 700 + 90 + 1
5   4985 ⬤ 4000 + 800 + 90 + 5
6   7004 ⬤ 7000 + 40
7 20 450 ⬤ 20 000 + 400 + 50 + 0
8 17 680 ⬤ 10 000 + 700 + 60 + 8

15

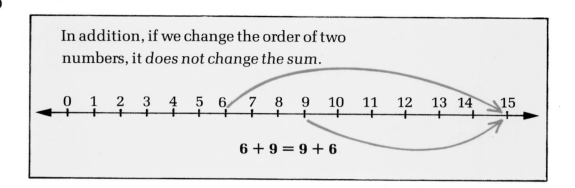

In addition, if we change the order of two numbers, it *does not change the sum.*

6 + 9 = 9 + 6

Solve these equations by finding the number which can be put in place of each letter.

1 6 + 8 = 8 + $\boxed{a}$
2 9 + 7 = 7 + $\boxed{v}$
3 15 + 13 = $\boxed{c}$ + 15
4 30 + $\boxed{r}$ = 40 + 30
5 19 + $\boxed{s}$ = 16 + 19
6 $\boxed{z}$ + 35 = 35 + 25
7 429 + 318 = $\boxed{e}$ + 429
8 967 + $\boxed{n}$ = 957 + 967

16

In addition, the way in which we group numbers *does not change the sum.*

We could add these first.

(4 + 5) + 6   or

9 + 6 = 15

We could add these first.

4 + (5 + 6)

4 + 11 = 15

Remember this useful law when finding the answers to the sums below.

28 + 7 + 3   Think: 28 + (7 + 3) = 28 + 10 = 38

1 8 + 6 + 4
2 6 + 4 + 15 + 5
3 17 + 5 + 15
4 16 + 4 + 17
5 7 + 43 + 9
6 35 + 5 + 18 + 2
7 46 + 4 + 23 + 7
8 22 + 8 + 14 + 6

17

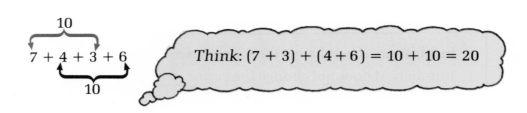

Think: $(7 + 3) + (4 + 6) = 10 + 10 = 20$

Find these sums.

1 $6 + 9 + 4$

2 $4 + 87 + 6$

3 $2 + 7 + 8 + 3$

4 $13 + 9 + 7 + 1$

5 $4 + 5 + 5 + 6$

6 $9 + 6 + 11 + 4$

7 $35 + 5 + 18 + 2$

8 $30 + 3 + 40 + 7$

18

Work out these additions.

1 $40 + 17 =$ ■

2 $48 + 14 =$ ■

3 $36 + 43 =$ ■

4 $80 + 40 =$ ■

5 £42 + £37 = £ ■

6 $60 + 49 =$ ■

7 $38 + 42 =$ ■

8 $77 + 50 =$ ■

19

Find these sums.

1 $613 + 80 =$ ■

2 $450 + \ \ 60 =$ ■

3 $340 + 38 =$ ■

4 $170 + 130 =$ ■

5 $180 + 20 =$ ■

6 $240 + 160 =$ ■

7 $190 + 30 =$ ■

8 $290 + 140 =$ ■

20

Do these additions.

1 $36 + 94 =$ ■

2 $78 + 99 =$ ■

3 $59 + 71 =$ ■

4 $85 + 97 =$ ■

5 $78 + 43 =$ ■

6 $64 + 98 =$ ■

7 $66 + 86 =$ ■

8 $48 + 96 =$ ■

21

1 Find the sum of all the even numbers between 3 and 9.
2 What is the total of eight, twenty-eight and twelve?
3 Seventy-three plus thirty-seven.
4 Add eight, nine and fourteen.
5 Find the total of all the odd numbers between 4 and 10.
6 Add fifty, sixty and ninety.
7 Find the number which is 600 greater than 1600.
8 What is the sum of 850, 67 and 3?

22

Find the difference between:

1 72 and 9.
2 51 and 12.
3 90 and 40.
4 73 and 46.
5 97 and 24.
6 96 and 38.
7 sixty and twenty-eight.
8 sixty-four and thirty-seven.

23

Do these subtractions.

1 $160 - 73 = $ ▣
2 $142 - 65 = $ ▣
3 $130 - 35 = $ ▣
4 $103 - 28 = $ ▣
5 $150 - 94 = $ ▣
6 $133 - 66 = $ ▣
7 $132 - 43 = $ ▣
8 $245 - 86 = $ ▣

24

Write each answer in digits.

1 Take eighty from three hundred and forty.
2 Take sixty from two hundred and thirty.
3 Take thirty from five hundred and ten.
4 Take seventy from four hundred and twenty.
5 Take one hundred and forty from three hundred and thirty.
6 Take two hundred and fifty from five hundred and ten.
7 Take one hundred and eighty from five hundred and forty.
8 Take four hundred and ninety from six hundred and sixty.

25

Write the answers to these subtractions in words.

1 Take 19 from 71.
2 What is the difference between 50 and 500?
3 Take 250 from 1000.
4 208 minus 109.
5 What must be added to 83 to make 300?
6 Take two hundred from two thousand.
7 What number is fifty less than five thousand?
8 Subtract 70 from 260.

26

Write out these equations, putting the correct
number in place of each ■.

1 $60 + ■ = 100$
2 $210 = 80 + ■$
3 $62 = 43 + ■$
4 $190 = 320 - ■$
5 $80 - ■ = 51$
6 $■ + 67 = 102$
7 $66 + ■ = 82$
8 $124 - ■ = 65$

27

Solve these equations.

1 $80 + 60 = 190 - \boxed{a}$
2 $320 - 60 = 290 - \boxed{c}$
3 $60 + 80 = 160 - \boxed{e}$
4 $330 - 70 = 300 - \boxed{n}$

Write $>$, $<$ or $=$ in place of each ●.

5 $46 + 15 ● 74 - 15$
6 $94 - 53 ● 80 - 39$
7 $432 + 234 ● 342 + 324$
8 $17 - 5 ● 10 + 4 + 2$

28

1 Look at the signpost. How far is it from Dantry to Clair Town?

2 What is the distance from Slipton to Dantry?

3 How far is Lea from Dring?

4 Work out the distance from Iving to Dantry.

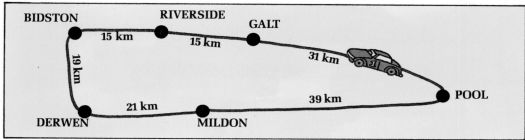

5 Look at the map of a car rally circuit shown above.
    What is the distance from Derwen through Mildon and Pool to Galt?

6 Find the distance from Pool through Bidston to Derwen.

7 How many kilometres more is the distance from Pool to
    Derwen than from Pool to Mildon?

8 How many kilometres is the whole circuit?

29

1 Take 17 from the sum of 14 and 19.

2 What must be added to 16 to equal 8 + 19?

3 From the sum of 3 and 5 subtract their difference.

4 Add the sum of 4 and 6 to the difference between 4 and 6.

5 How many more than 50 is the total of 7, 17 and 27?

6 The sum of two numbers is 9 and their difference is 1.
    What are the numbers?

7 A cricketer needed 17 runs for his half century (50).
    How many runs had he scored?

8 A boy cycled 100 kilometres in 3 days.
    The first day he cycled 37 kilometres.
    and the last day he cycled 28 kilometres.
    How many kilometres did he cycle on the second day?

30

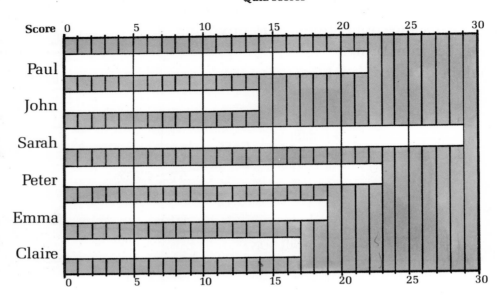

Quiz scores

Use the **bar chart** above to answer these questions.

1 What was the difference between the highest and lowest scores?
2 How many more than John did Paul score?
3 The perfect score was 30. How many points did Sarah lose?
4 What was the total score of the boys?
5 What was the total score of the girls?
6 Who won – the boys or the girls – and by how many?
7 What was the total score of Paul, Sarah and Claire?
8 What was the total of the two highest scores?

31

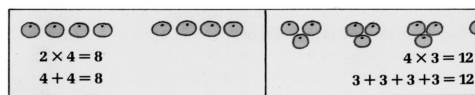

$2 \times 4 = 8$
$4 + 4 = 8$

$4 \times 3 = 12$
$3 + 3 + 3 + 3 = 12$

Look at the examples above.

Now write a multiplication equation and an addition equation for each of these.

1

2

3

4

5

6

7

8

32

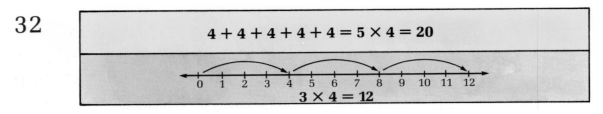

$$4 + 4 + 4 + 4 + 4 = 5 \times 4 = 20$$

$$3 \times 4 = 12$$

Write a multiplication equation for each of the additions and number lines.

1 $4 + 4 + 4 + 4 + 4 + 4 + 4 + 4 + 4$

2 $9 + 9 + 9 + 9 + 9 + 9 + 9$

3 $6 + 6 + 6 + 6 + 6 + 6 + 6 + 6$

4 $3 + 3 + 3 + 3 + 3$

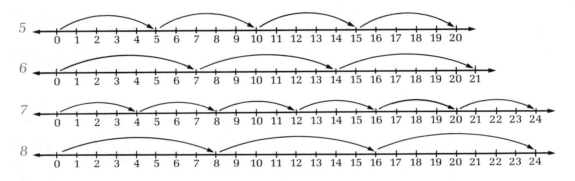

33

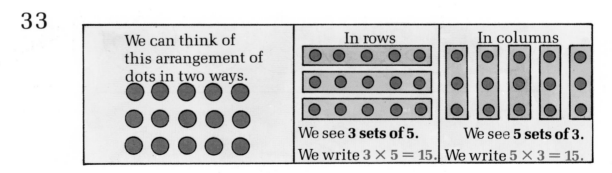

We can think of this arrangement of dots in two ways.

In rows

We see **3 sets of 5.**
We write $3 \times 5 = 15.$

In columns

We see **5 sets of 3.**
We write $5 \times 3 = 15.$

Now write two multiplication equations for each of these drawings.

1

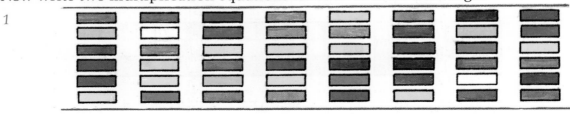

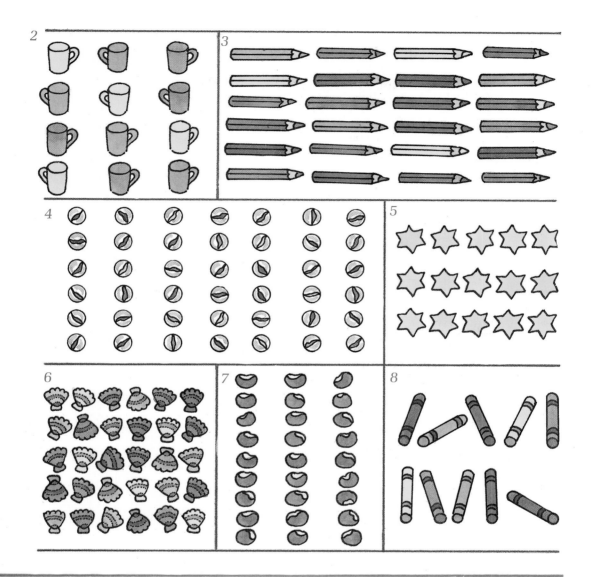

34

Write out these statements, putting the correct number

in place of each ■ and ▲.

1 21 = 7 × ■ or ■ × ▲   2 35 = 7 × ■ or ■ × ▲

3 33 = 11 × ■ or ■ × ▲   4 42 = 6 × ■ or ■ × ▲

5 14 = 7 × ■ or ■ × ▲   6 77 = 7 × ■ or ■ × ▲

7 55 = 11 × ■ or ■ × ▲   8 15 = 3 × ■ or ■ × ▲

35

1 Find half of nine thousand and write the answer in digits.
2 $(6 \times 7) + 8 = \boxed{n}$. What number does $\boxed{n}$ stand for?
3 Find the total of $7 + 7 + 7 + 3 + 3 + 3 + 3$.
4 $607 + 170 + 7000 = \blacksquare$
5 Five times a certain number is half of fifty. What is the number?
6 The sum of two numbers is 11 and their difference is 3. What are the numbers?
7 Multiply 9 by 13.

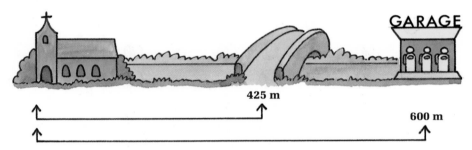

8 What is the distance from the bridge to the garage?

36

> The **product** of 7 and 4 is 28.
> 7 and 4 are **factors** of 28.
>
> The **product** of 3 and 5 is 15.
> 3 and 5 are **factors** of 15.

Every number has 1 as a factor and every number has itself as a factor, eg the only factors of 13 are 1 and 13.

1 What are the factors of 21? (Don't include 1 and 21.)
2 What is the product of 5 and 9?
3 Find the product of 3, 2 and 5.
4 What number, besides 1, is a factor of 35 and 28?
5 What number, besides 1, is a factor of both 35 and 75?
6 Which of these numbers is a factor of $84 - 5, 9, 7, 8$?
7 Work out the product of 17 and 10.
8 Find the sum of the factors of 77. (Don't forget to include 1 and 77.)

37

We know that the order in which numbers are added makes no difference to the sum.
Does the order in which numbers are grouped for multiplication make any difference to the product?

$(4 \times 2) \times 5 = 40$ $4 \times (2 \times 5) = 40$ $(4 \times 5) \times 2 = 40$

Remember this useful law when finding these products.

1 $5 \times 2 \times 6 = $ ■

2 $19 \times 5 \times 2 = $ ■

3 $7 \times 2 \times 5 = $ ■

4 $2 \times 17 \times 5 = $ ■

5 $3 \times 4 \times 5 = $ ■

6 $6 \times 3 \times 5 \times 2 = $ ■

7 $6 \times 2 \times 50 = $ ■

8 $3 \times 2 \times 5 \times 3 = $ ■

38

17×10 means 17 tens $= 170$

23×100 means 23 hundreds $= 2300$

1 $37 \times 10 = $ ■

2 $10 \times 49 = $ ■

3 $65 \times 10 = $ ■

4 $100 \times 19 = $ ■

5 $14 \times 100 = $ ■

6 $49 \times 100 = $ ■

7 $23 \times 1000 = $ ■

8 $1000 \times 14 = $ ■

39

Since	then
$7 \times 4 = 28$	7×40 means 28 tens $= 280$

1 $9 \times 40 = $ ■

2 $6 \times 30 = $ ■

3 $7 \times 80 = $ ■

4 $60 \times 4 = $ ■

5 $2 \times 600 = $ ■

6 $700 \times 5 = $ ■

7 $3000 \times 7 = $ ■

8 $9 \times 5000 = $ ■

40

1 About how many marbles are there in the jar on the right?
Choose the best estimate.

      (20   200   2000   20 000)

2 Take one-third of ninety from half of ninety-two.

3 To the sum of 500 and 50 add the difference between 500 and 50.

4 If $\boxed{n}$ + 15 = 200, then $\boxed{n}$ = ■.

5 479 + 99 = ■

6 (8 × 8) + ■ = 80

7 Add the product of 3 and 9 to the product of 7 and 9.

8 Copy and write the correct sign (= or ≠) in place of ●.

        8 × 9 ● 50 + 22

---

41   Study these examples first.

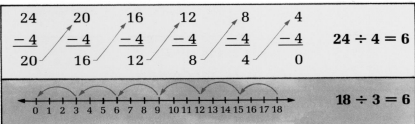

$$24 \div 4 = 6$$

$$18 \div 3 = 6$$

Now write a division equation for each of these.

1

35	28	21	14	7
− 7	− 7	− 7	− 7	− 7
28	21	14	7	0

2

54	45	36	27	18	9
− 9	− 9	− 9	− 9	− 9	− 9
45	36	27	18	9	0

3

64	56	48	40	32	24	16	8
− 8	− 8	− 8	− 8	− 8	− 8	− 8	− 8
56	48	40	32	24	16	8	0

4

42	36	30	24	18	12	6
− 6	− 6	− 6	− 6	− 6	− 6	− 6
36	30	24	18	12	6	0

5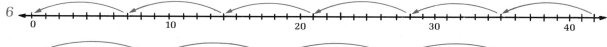

6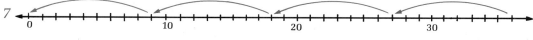

7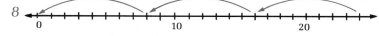

8

42

We have already learned that we can write a division example like this: $\frac{24}{8}$. This is known as the **fractional form**. Remember the answer in a division is called the **quotient**.

Find the quotient in these.

1 $\frac{49}{7}$ 2 $\frac{56}{7}$ 3 $\frac{54}{6}$ 4 $\frac{48}{8}$

5 $\frac{72}{8}$ 6 $\frac{63}{9}$ 7 $\frac{81}{9}$ 8 $\frac{32}{4}$

43

1 How many elevens are there in 110?

2 Divide 240 by 4.

3 Find a third of two hundred and ten.

4 What is the remainder when 77 is divided by 9?

5 $180 \div 6 = $ ▨

6 $560 \div 7 = $ ▨

7 $2100 \div 3 = $ ▨

8 $300 \div 60 = $ ▨

44

Find the quotient and remainder in each of these divisions, like this:

$$47 \div 5 = 9 \text{ r } 2$$

1 $77 \div 9 = $ ■ r ▲
2 $69 \div 7 = $ ■ r ▲
3 $60 \div 8 = $ ■ r ▲
4 $34 \div 7 = $ ■ r ▲
5 $104 \div 30 = $ ■ r ▲
6 $267 \div 50 = $ ■ r ▲
7 $400 \div 60 = $ ■ r ▲
8 $150 \div 40 = $ ■ r ▲

45

1 If 20 drinking straws are used
   each day, how long will a full box last?

2 Look how these numbers grow.
   Now write down the next two numbers.

   800, 850, 900, 950, ■, ■

3 487 is ■ less than $\frac{1}{2}$ of 1000.

4 What is the difference between 70 and 700?

5 What is the quotient: $240 \div 80$?

6 Find the product of 60 and 20.

7 Find the sum of 280 and 70.

8 When full, this jug holds 1000 millilitres.
   How many millilitres are in the jug now?

46

Mark has 5 marbles, Sam
1 marble and David 6.
If they put all their marbles
together and shared them
equally, they would each
have four marbles.
The **average** of 5, 1 and 6 is 4.

Mark   ⊘⊘⊘⊖⊘
Sam   ⊘
David   ⊗⊘⊗⊘⊘⊘

Mark   ⊗⊘⊘⊘
Sam   ⊘⊘⊘⊘
David   ⊗⊘⊘⊘

1 Find the average number
   of flowers in a vase.

2 What is the average number of matches in a set?

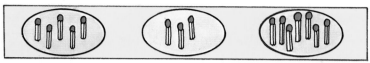

3 What is the average number of books on a shelf?

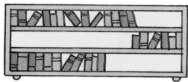

4 Four children completed a jigsaw puzzle.
Here are the times taken in minutes.
Find the average time.

Paul	Mira	Usha	Lisa
35	30	30	25

5 A motorist travelled 100 kilometres on Monday, 50 kilometres
on Tuesday and 90 kilometres on Wednesday.
What was the average distance travelled in a day?

6 Find the average of 10, 5, 6, 1 and 3.

7 There are 10 classes in Park View School and there is
an average of 27 pupils in a class. How many pupils
are in the school?

8 What is the average age of these girls?

Karen	Sarah	Emma
10	5	12

47

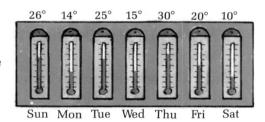

| | 26° | 14° | 25° | 15° | 30° | 20° | 10° |
| Sun | Mon | Tue | Wed | Thu | Fri | Sat |

1 These thermometers show the temperature
at 9 o'clock each day for a week.
What is the average daily temperature?

2 Here are the weights of three children
in kilograms. What is the average weight?

Salim	Ali	Claire
35	30	55

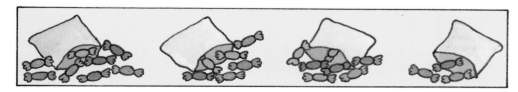

3 Find the average number of sweets in a bag.

Team A	Team B	Team C
8	12	13

4 Work out the average number of goals scored by these three netball teams.

5 The record on the right shows the time it took David to walk to school. Work out his average time.

MON	20 minutes
TUE	25 minutes
WED	25 minutes
THU	15 minutes
FRI	15 minutes

6 Find the average of 43 and 57.

7 Work out the average of these numbers.

15, 15, 40 and 50

8 The average age of three boys is 10 years. Philip is 7 years and Brian 11 years. How old is David?

48

We have already learned that the Romans used seven main symbols to write numbers.

1	5	10	50	100	500	1000
I	V	X	L	C	D	M

To find the value of a number we must add the value of the numerals, like this:

XVIII = 10 + 5 + 1 + 1 + 1 = 18

CCXXXIII = 100 + 100 + 10 + 10 + 10 + 1 + 1 + 1 = 233

Write these numbers in our numerals.

1 XXVI 2 XXXVIII 3 CCCXVI 4 DCXX

5 Write 700 in Roman numerals.

6 Write 81 in Roman numerals.

7 Write 126 in Roman numerals.

8 Write 1101 in Roman numerals.

1	I
2	II
3	III
4	IV
5	V
6	VI
7	VII
8	VIII
9	IX
10	X
11	XI
12	XII
13	XIII
14	XIV
15	XV
16	XVI
17	XVII
18	XVIII
19	XIX
20	XX

49

The Romans rarely used the same four symbols together.

> Instead of **IIII** for four, they wrote **IV** (5 − 1).
> Instead of **VIIII** for nine, they wrote **IX** (10 − 1).
> Instead of **XXXX** for forty, they wrote **XL** (50 − 10).
> Instead of **LXXXX** for ninety, they wrote **XC** (100 − 10).

1 Write XXIV in our numerals.

2 Write XXXIX in our numerals.

3 Write CXL in our numerals.

4 Write LXIV in our numerals.

5 Write 94 in Roman numerals.

6 Write 46 in Roman numerals.

7 Write 900 in Roman numerals.

8 Write 944 in Roman numerals.

50

1 Write in digits the number which is 1010 more than 9990.

2 What number can be written in place of in this subtraction?

$$\begin{array}{r} \blacksquare \\ -\ 9\ 9 \\ \hline 1\ 0\ 9 \end{array}$$

3 Solve this equation:

$60 + 39 + \boxed{a} = 139.$

4 Which sign (+, −, × or ÷) should be placed instead of ▲ in this equation?

$350 + 650 = 925\ \blacktriangle\ 75$

5 Find $\frac{1}{3}$ of the difference between 11 and 110.

6 Look how these numbers grow. Write the next two numbers.

35   70   105   140   ■   ■

7 What is the distance from Paris to Claye?

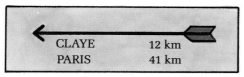

CLAYE   12 km
PARIS   41 km

8 I am thinking of a certain number. If I add this number to itself then add 50, I get 100. What is the number?

51

1 What is the score on the dartboard?

2 A third of a certain number is equal to a quarter of twelve.
   What is the number?

3 Write the correct symbol (>, < or =) in place of 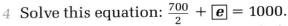.
   $$60 + 1300 + 7 \bullet 1476$$

4 Solve this equation: $\frac{700}{2} + \boxed{e} = 1000$.

5 An aircraft flew at an average speed of 2000 kilometres per hour for $2\frac{1}{4}$ hours.
   How far did it fly?

6 When a certain number is divided by 9, the quotient is 5
   and the remainder is 5. What is the number?

7 Write 99 in Roman numerals.

8 Claire has 15 pages of foreign stamps with 20 stamps on each page.
   How many stamps does she have?

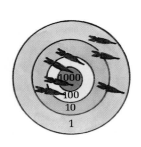

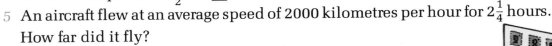

52

1 Write a numeral for the number that means 10 thousands,
   0 hundreds, 4 tens and 2 units.

2 A clock strikes the hours only. How many times does it strike in half a day?
   Work it out like this: 12 + 11 + 10 + 9 . . .

3 Complete the sentence below.
   The product of 6 and 3 is the same as the sum of 9 and ■.

4 What number when multiplied by 9 is 7 less than 70?

5 During a traffic count John noted twice as many cars as other vehicles.
   He counted 46 cars. How many vehicles did he count altogether?

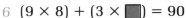

Traffic Count	
CARS	⊺⊦⊦ I
LORRIES	⊺⊦⊦ I
BUSES	⊺⊦⊦ I
VANS	III

6 $(9 \times 8) + (3 \times \blacksquare) = 90$

7 $65 + 19 + 35 + 11 = \blacksquare$

8 5400 eggs. How many boxes?

53

1 Write a numeral for this
number of pencils.

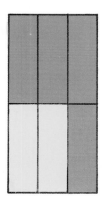

2 $(6 \times 9) + 7 = $ ▪

3 The sum of two numbers is 1000. One of the numbers is 90. What is the other?

4 Here are the distances in kilometres cycled by Sarah in a week.
What was her daily average?

Sun	Mon	Tue	Wed	Thu	Fri	Sat
13	7	16	4	19	1	10

5 Solve this equation: $\frac{n}{6} = \frac{1}{3}$ of 9.

6 What fraction of the shape on the right is coloured red?

7 What is the sum of the two odd numbers greater than 25
and less than 30?

8 There are 7 shelves with an average of 150 books to a shelf.
How many books are there?

54

1 What is the difference between these calculator numbers?

2 Calculate the product of these calculator numbers.

3 Use the smaller number as the divisor. What is the quotient?

4 Find twice the sum of these two numbers.

5 What is $\frac{1}{7}$ of the larger number?

6 Write the larger number in Roman numerals.

7 What fraction of the larger number is the smaller number?

8 Work out the average of the two numbers.

55

1 What is the largest number you can name using each of these digits once: 4, 3, 6, 1?

2 Find $1\frac{1}{2}$ times 70.

3 $(7 \times 6) +$ ▨ $= 54$

4 Write a fraction to tell which part of this picture is red.

5 Write this number in our own numerals.   CCCLX

6 $1000 = 550 +$ ▨

7 At a party there were 7 boys and 9 girls. If they each ate an average of 4 mince pies, how many were eaten altogether?

8 Find one-fifth of the sum of thirty-four and twenty-six.

56

Here is a penny and a two pence coin.

Find the value in pence of each of these rows of coins.

1

▨p

2

▨p

3

p

4

p

5 How many twos are equal in value to 22 pennies?
6 How many pennies are equal in value to 40 twos?
7 How many twos are equal in value to 50 pennies?
8 What is the value in pence of 9 twos and 9 pennies?

57

7p each

APPLES

1 How many of these apples
   could you buy with the
   coins shown?
2 How many of these apples
   could you buy with 7 twos
   and 7 pennies?
3 How many of these apples could you buy with 8 pennies and 10 twos?
4 David paid for 5 apples with 15 twos and the rest in pennies.
   How many pennies did he give?

5 Krishna paid for one of these
oranges with 3 twos and the
rest in pennies. How many
coins did she give?

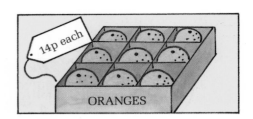

6 How many twos are needed
to pay for 3 of these oranges?

7 How many twos would you need to pay for 2 of the
apples and one of the oranges?

8 How many twos would be needed to pay for all the oranges?

58

Here is a ten pence coin, called a **ten**, and a five pence coin, called a **five**.

Find the value in pence of each of these rows of coins.

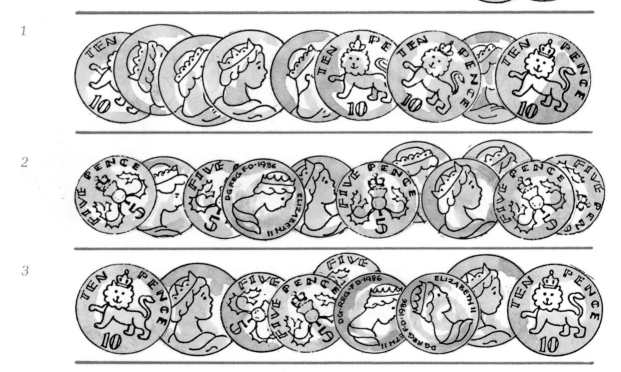

1

2

3

4 How many tens are the same value as 60p?

5 How many fives are the same value as 75p?

6 How many fives must be paid for 7 eggs?

7 How many tens are the same value as 6 fives?

8 Lisa paid for 6 eggs with 3 tens and the rest in fives.
   How many fives did she give?

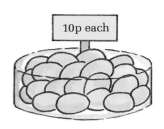

10p each

59

Here is a twenty pence coin, called a **twenty**.

Find the value in pence of each row of coins.

1   ▢p

2   ▢p

3 How many twenties are equal in value to 8 fives?

4 How many twenties are equal in value to 4 tens and 4 fives?

38

Find the value of the coins in each of the boxes below.

5 ▮p

6 ▮p

7 ▮p

8 ▮p

60

1 Look at the abacus. If I moved a bead from the units place to the thousands place, by how many would I increase the number?

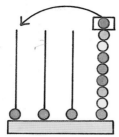

2 Increase the sum of 87 and 96 by 13.
3 The boys ran twice round the field.
What distance did they run?

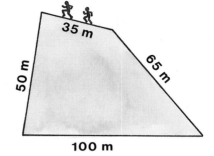

4 $20 \times 0 \times 50 = \blacksquare$
5 What fraction of this shape is red?

6 Write $>$, $<$ or $=$ in place of ⬤.
$$6 \times 5 \ ⬤ \ 5 \times (4 + 2)$$

7 What is the highest possible total score after 3 throws of these dice?
8 The product of two numbers is the same as their sum.
What are the two numbers?

61

Give the value in pence of:
1 3 tens and 4 fives.
2 9 tens and 4 twos.
3 1 twenty, 6 fives and 4 twos.
4 6 tens and 20 pennies.
5 2 twenties, 7 fives and 20 pennies.
6 7 fives and 15 twos.
7 2 twenties, 5 twos and 10 pennies.
8 6 tens, 6 fives and 6 pennies.

62

Write these in full.

1 64p = 3 tens and ☐ twos
2 99p = 7 tens and ☐ pennies
3 67p = ☐ twenties, 1 five and 1 two
4 39p = ☐ fives, 6 twos and 7 pennies
5 87p = ☐ tens, 5 fives and 22 pennies
6 38p = ☐ fives and 9 twos
7 84p = 3 twenties, ☐ fives and 9 pennies
8 70p = 3 tens, 3 fives and ☐ pennies

63

Here is a fifty pence coin, called a **fifty**.

1 How many tens are equal in value to 2 fifties?
2 How many twenties are equal in value to a fifty and a ten?
3 How many fives are equal in value to 5 fifties?
4 How many twos are equal in value to 4 fifties?
5 50p = 1 ten, 1 five and ☐ pennies
6 50p = 1 twenty, 1 five, 5 twos and ☐ pennies

7

= ☐ p

8

= ☐ p

64

£7·49 means **7 pounds and 49 pence**.

We say **seven pounds forty-nine**.

Write these amounts using the £ sign.

1 thirty pounds thirty
2 six pounds nineteen
3 eighteen pounds eight
4 ten pounds seventy-five

twenty-eight pounds ninety-nine

Write the amounts on these price labels in words.

5

£16·60

6

£19·03

7

£30·10

8

£30·15

65

1 Find half of nineteen thousand and write the numeral in digits.
2 On a certain day 35 aircraft flew into Heathrow Airport every hour. How many landed between 08 00 and 12 00?
3 Subtract five hundred and five from a thousand.
4 What is the sum of the numbers greater than 12 and less than 20 which are divisible by 3?
5 Find a quarter of the product of sixteen and ten.
6 The total of three numbers is 50. Two of the numbers are 18 and 23. What is the other number?

Birthday money

7 The pie chart shows how Jennifer spent her £12 birthday money. How much did she spend on a ring?
8 a How much did Jennifer spend on a calculator?
  b How much did the pen cost?

66

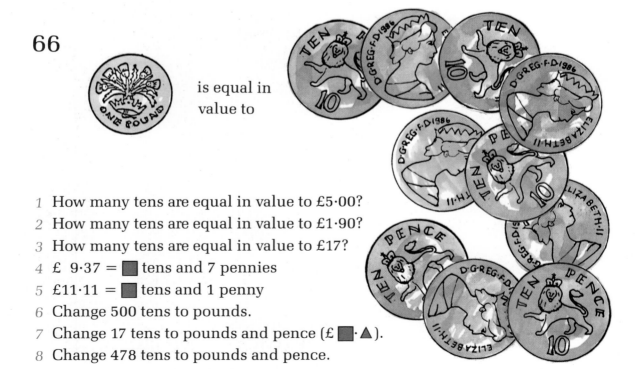

is equal in value to

1 How many tens are equal in value to £5·00?
2 How many tens are equal in value to £1·90?
3 How many tens are equal in value to £17?
4 £ 9·37 = ▢ tens and 7 pennies
5 £11·11 = ▢ tens and 1 penny
6 Change 500 tens to pounds.
7 Change 17 tens to pounds and pence (£ ▢·▲).
8 Change 478 tens to pounds and pence.

67  is equal in value to

1 How many twenties are equal in value to £4·00?
2 How many twenties are equal in value to £1·20?
3 How many twenties are equal in value to £10·00?
4 How many twenties are equal in value to £9·40?
5 £2·45 = ▉ twenties and 5 pennies
6 Change 10 twenties to pounds.
7 Change 7 twenties to pounds and pence.
8 Change 50 twenties to pounds.

68

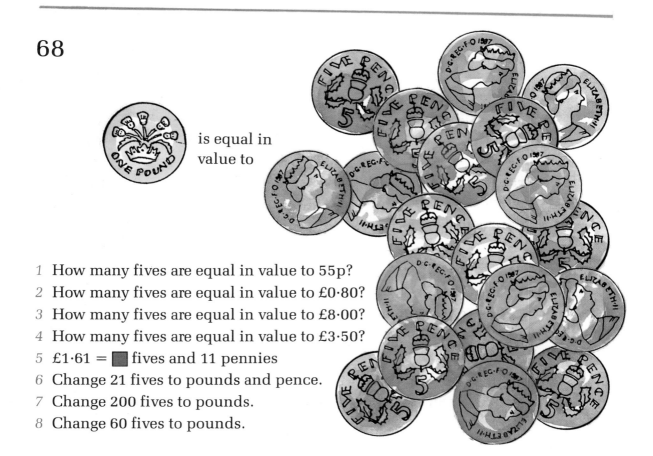

is equal in value to

1 How many fives are equal in value to 55p?
2 How many fives are equal in value to £0·80?
3 How many fives are equal in value to £8·00?
4 How many fives are equal in value to £3·50?
5 £1·61 = ▉ fives and 11 pennies
6 Change 21 fives to pounds and pence.
7 Change 200 fives to pounds.
8 Change 60 fives to pounds.

69

is equal in value to

1 How many twos are equal in value to 28p?
2 How many twos are equal in value to £0·70?
3 How many twos are equal in value to £5?
4 How many twos are equal in value to £1·60?
5 Change 90 twos to pounds and pence.
6 Change 150 twos to pounds.
7 Change 55 twos to pounds and pence.
8 Change 200 twos to pounds.

70

1 How many eggs are there?
  Write the numeral in words.
2 $(6 \times 8) \times (10 \times 10) = \blacksquare$
3 Which number, apart from 1,
  is a factor of 28, 56 and 63?
4 Write the correct symbol ($<$, $>$ or $=$) in place of ⬤.

  $$37 + 73 \ ⬤ \ 173 - 37$$

5 In this equation each triangle (▲) stands for the same number.
  Write out the equation, putting the number in place of the triangles.

  $$▲ + ▲ + ▲ = 120$$

6 $\frac{1}{9}$ of 54 $= \frac{1}{4}$ of $\blacksquare$

7 Salim needs 25 more coins to fill his coin album.
  His album has 10 pages with 12 coin spaces on each page.
  How many coins does he have now?

8 How many tens are equal in value to 10 twos, 10 fives and 10 pennies?

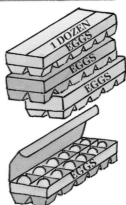

71

 is equal in value to

1. How many fifties are the same value as £5·00?
2. How many fifties are the same value as £16?
3. How many fifties are the same value as £17·50?
4. How many fifties are the same value as 10 twenties?
5. Change 18 fifties to pounds.
6. Change 27 fifties to pounds and pence.
7. Change 101 fifties to pounds and pence.
8. Change 50 fifties to pounds.

72

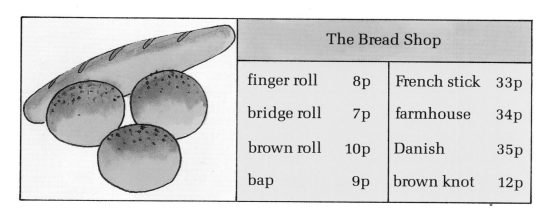

The Bread Shop			
finger roll	8p	French stick	33p
bridge roll	7p	farmhouse	34p
brown roll	10p	Danish	35p
bap	9p	brown knot	12p

1. Find the total cost of a French stick, a farmhouse loaf and a Danish loaf.
2. What must be paid for a bridge roll, a French stick and a brown knot?
3. How much must I pay for 2 finger rolls, 2 bridge rolls and 2 brown rolls?
4. What is the total cost of 2 French sticks and a farmhouse loaf?

5 Mira spent 50p at the bread shop. She bought a Danish loaf and a bridge roll.
   What else did she buy?

6 David was given a twenty change. He had bought a finger roll,
   a brown roll and a brown knot. What had he given the shopkeeper?

7 Susan was given a ten change after buying 10 baps.
   How much had she given the shopkeeper?

8 Ali bought a bridge roll and a French stick. Ahmed bought
   a brown roll and a bap.
   How much did the two boys pay altogether?

73

1 What must be paid for a front light and a mirror?
2 What is the total cost of a mirror and a horn?
3 Work out the total cost of a flag and a speedometer?
4 Find the total cost of a horn and a flag?
5 How much is a light and a speedometer?
6 £1·15 + £4·30 + £2·45 = £ ▣
7 £2·30 + £1·60 + £0·70 = £ ▣
8 £0·50 + £1·36 + £4·14 = £ ▣

74

> Remember if a total in pence is equal to or greater than 100, show the amount using the decimal point and the £ sign.

Add these amounts.

1 79p + 31p = £ ▢
2 £0·94 + £0·16 = £ ▢
3 62p + 77p = £ ▢
4 £0·63 + £0·57 = £ ▢
5 £0·88 + £0·42 = £ ▢
6 40p + 80p + 60p = £ ▢
7 £0·75 + £0·35 + £0·60 = £ ▢
8 £0·39 + £0·46 + £0·24 = £ ▢

75

1 Write in digits forty thousand and forty.
2 Solve this equation: 650 + $\boxed{n}$ = 1700.
3 Write the correct symbol (>, < or =) in place of ●.

$18 \div 6 \, ● \, 3 \times (2 + 1)$

4 The sum of 47 and 16 is equal to the product of 7 and ▪.
   What is the missing number?
5 Add the product of 3 and 8 to the product of 7 and 8.
6 Find the average of these numbers:

7 How many fives are equal in value to 3 tens, 7 twos and 1 penny?
8 A lady paid for this writing case with 20 fifties and the rest in fives.
   How many fives did she give?

£10·55

76

Find the difference between these amounts.

1 70p and 23p
2 £0·19 and £0·91
3 £0·60 and £0·06
4 £0·23 and £0·32
5 93p and 39p

6 How much more is the dog jigsaw than the duck **jigsaw** ?

7 How much less is the train jigsaw than the duck **jigsaw** ?

8 How much more than the train jigsaw is the dog jigsaw?

77

Work out your change if you spend:

1 17p out of a fifty.

2 £0·50 out of a five pound note.

3 53p out of 3 twenties.

4 £2·50 out of a ten pound note.

5 £0·14 out of £1·00.

6 £3·30 out of £5·00.

7 £0·89 out of 2 fifties.

8 £17·90 out of £20·00.

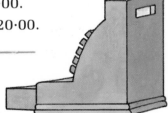

78

1 Take 20p from £3·10.

2 How much less than £1·40 is 60p?

3 What is left when 90p is taken from £1·50?

4 What must be added to 70p to make £4·20?

5 Subtract 46p from £2·06.

6 If I had 80p more, I would have £13. How much do I have now?

7 Find the difference between nine pounds and ninety pence.

8 £2·60 − 70p = £ ▇

79

Find the difference between these amounts.

1 £4·70 and £2·40

2 £4·50 and £2·60

3 £3·60 and £1·59

4 £7·39 and £6·10

5 £50 and £5·50

6 £5·10 and £4·80

7 £4·90 and £1·75

8 £11·45 and £10·50

80

1 There are fifteen shelves and there are two hundred books on each shelf. How many thousands of books are there altogether?
2 Write these numbers in order from the least to the greatest.

    1100   1010   1001   1101   1011

3 Write the correct symbol (= or ≠) in place of ⬤.

    56 ÷ 8 ⬤ 63 ÷ 7

4 What must be added to 644 to make 1044?
5 Write this chapter number in words.

> CHAPTER
> **LXI**

6 Jaswant bought 4 pencils at 15p each and paid the exact amount with two coins. What were the coins?
7 A school is allowed to make one educational visit in the morning and one in the afternoon.
How many different ways are there of spending the day?

Morning	Afternoon
Tower of London	Science Museum
London Zoo	Planetarium
Heathrow Airport	Cutty Sark

8 A bank changed a twenty pound note into twenties. How many coins were there?

81

party hats	9p
trumpets	7p
blow-outs	3p
streamers	6 for 7p
balloons	3 for 10p
masks	20p
whistles	5p
funny noses	8p

Find the cost of these party novelties.
1 ten funny noses
2 a dozen trumpets
3 eleven party hats
4 thirty balloons
5 twelve streamers
6 forty blow-outs
7 ten masks
8 twenty whistles

82

Work out the cost of these.

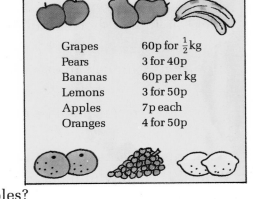

Grapes	60p for $\frac{1}{2}$ kg
Pears	3 for 40p
Bananas	60p per kg
Lemons	3 for 50p
Apples	7p each
Oranges	4 for 50p

1 $\frac{1}{2}$ dozen lemons

2 a dozen pears

3 12 oranges

4 six apples

5 3 kg of bananas

6 2 kg of grapes

7 How much more do 6 pears cost than 6 apples?

8 1 kg of grapes costs as much as how many pears?

83

A sports and leisure centre bought games and sports equipment.
Find the cost of each of these.

1 2 chess sets at £8·80 each

2 2 table tennis sets at £5·60 a set

3 4 pairs of skates at £15·50 a pair

4 2 dart boards at £9·99 each

5 5 tennis rackets at £20·20 each

6 4 junior hockey sticks at £10·25 each

7 6 sets of dominoes at £2·20 a set

8 9 footballs at £10·30 each

84

A school science club bought some equipment.

Find the cost of each of these.

1 3 electric buzzers at 99p each

2 4 electric motors at £2·25 each

3 11 magnets at 30p each

4 24 bulbs at 50p each

5 3 DD batteries

6 2 AA batteries

7 4 CC batteries

8 9 BB batteries

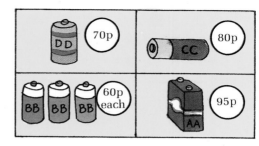

85

1 Add five hundred to this calculator number.

2 By how many is the product of 20 and 20 less than a thousand?

3 How many fifties are there in seven hundred and fifty?

4 $(9 \times 6) + (6 \times 9) = $ ■

5 Find the average of Salim's cricket scores.

6 John had 500 conkers. He placed 60 conkers
in each of 7 bags. How many conkers were left over?

7 How much change is there from 3 fifties after spending £1·09?

8 What fraction of these shapes is red?

1st innings	|||| |||| |||| |||
2nd innings	|||| |||

86

1 Three drawing pencils cost 42p. What is the cost of one?

2 If 85p is shared equally among 5 boys, how much does each boy get?

3 Find one-sixth of £0·54.

4 Nine postage stamps of the same price cost £1·80.
What was the cost of 1 stamp?

5 £0·84 ÷ 7 = ■ p

6 A girl bought three records for £6·15.
What was the cost of one record?

7 Jane had £1·10 and gave half to her brother.
How many pence had she left?

8 Work out the cost of 1 concert ticket if 9 cost £8·10.

87

1 40p ÷ 4 = ■ p

2 £1·20 ÷ 2 = £■

3 66p ÷ 3 = ■ p

4 £2·80 ÷ 7 = £■

5 £0·72 ÷ 8 = £■

6 £6·40 ÷ 8 = £■

7 £0·96 ÷ 6 = £■

8 £9·63 ÷ 9 = £■

88

If we know the cost of 1, it is easy to find the cost of 10.

Look at these examples:

1 apple costs 8p	10 apples cost 80p	X 10
1 puzzle costs £0·09	10 puzzles cost £0·90	
1 eraser costs £0·19	10 erasers cost £1·90	

1 If 1 costs 7p, 10 cost £ ■.

2 If 1 costs 15p, 10 cost ■ p.

3 If 1 costs £0·06, 10 cost £ ■.

4 If 1 costs £0·19, 10 cost £ ■.

5 If 1 costs 15p, 10 cost £ ■.

6 If 1 costs £0·43, 10 cost £ ■.

7 If 1 costs £1·50, 10 cost £ ■.

8 If 1 costs £1·11, 10 cost £ ■.

89

If we know the cost of 10, it is easy to find the cost of 1. Look at these examples:

10 pencils cost £2·00	1 pencil costs £0·20	÷ 10
10 crayons cost £0·80	1 crayon costs £0·08	
10 pens cost £1·70	1 pen costs £0·17	

1 If 10 cost 90p, 1 costs ■ p.

2 If 10 cost £1·20, 1 costs ■ p.

3 If 10 cost £4·00, 1 costs £ ■.

4 If 10 cost £1·10, 1 costs £ ■.

5 If 10 cost £7·80, 1 costs £ ■.

6 If 10 cost £68·50, 1 costs £ ■.

7 If 10 cost £13·30, 1 costs £ ■.

8 If 10 cost £36·00, 1 costs £ ■.

90

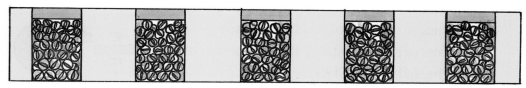

1. A boy found there was an average of 120 marbles in a jar.
   How many marbles were there altogether?
2. The product of three numbers is a thousand. If two of the numbers
   are 20 and 10, what is the other number?
3. 37 boys and 23 girls visited Windsor Castle in two coaches.
   If 35 travelled in the first coach, how many children were in the second coach?
4. Mr Martin is 48 years old. He is three times as old as his son, Robert.
   How old will Robert be in three years time?
5. Divide the product of 5 and 10 by the difference between 5 and 10.
6. $36 \times 20 = $ ☐
7. Eggs are 9p each or £1 a dozen. How much can you save by buying a dozen?
8. How many pears at 12p each can be bought with
   1 twenty, 1 ten, 1 five and 1 penny?

91

If we know the cost of 1, it is easy to find the cost of 100.

Look at these examples:

1 stamp costs 9p	100 stamps cost £9
1 stamp costs 20p	100 stamps cost £20
1 stamp costs £0·17	100 stamps cost £17·00
1 stamp costs £0·09	100 stamps cost £9·00

×100

1. If 1 costs 90p, 100 cost £ ☐.
2. If 1 costs 5p, 100 cost £ ☐.
3. If 1 costs 17p, 100 cost £ ☐.
4. If 1 costs 23p, 100 cost £ ☐.
5. If 1 costs £0·07, 100 cost £ ☐.
6. If 1 costs £0·39, 100 cost £ ☐.
7. If 1 costs £1·32, 100 cost £ ☐.
8. If 1 costs £2·30, 100 cost £ ☐.

92

If we know the cost of 100, it is easy to find the cost of 1.

Look at these examples:

100 metres of ribbon cost £5·00	1 metre costs 5p	
100 metres of rayon cost £11·00	1 metre costs 11p	÷100
100 metres of braid cost £135	1 metre costs £1·35	

1 If 100 cost £7, 1 costs p.
2 If 100 cost £3·00, 1 costs £ ■.
3 If 100 cost £19, 1 costs ■ p.
4 If 100 cost £14·00, 1 costs £ ■.
5 If 100 cost £90·00, 1 costs £ ■.
6 If 100 cost £110·00, 1 costs £ ■.
7 If 100 cost £350, 1 costs £ ■.
8 If 100 cost £965, 1 costs £ ■.

93

1 How many rockets costing 70p each can be bought for £7·00?
2 Catherine Wheels cost 30p each. How many can be bought for £1·80?
3 Roman Candles are 25p each. How many can you buy for £10?
4 How many packets of coloured sparklers costing 30p a packet can be bought for £6?
5 Fountains cost 60p each. How many can be bought for £60?
6 How many bangers costing 16p each can be bought with 4 twenties?
7 How many Little Demons at 3 for 40p can be bought for £2?
8 Meteors cost 40p. How many can be bought for £4·40?

94

1 How many slices of water melon can be bought for £1·25?
2 How many kilograms of grapes can be bought for £4·00?
3 How many peaches can be bought for £20?
4 A lady bought diaries for Christmas presents.
  If diaries cost 90p, how many did she buy for £6·30?
5 How many notebooks at 20p each can be bought for £10.
6 I gave 3 fifties for Christmas cards costing 30p each.
  How many did I buy?
7 Peter spent 80p a day during his camping holiday.
  How long did £16·00 last him?
8 A school spent £190 on maths books costing £1·90 each.
  How many books were bought?

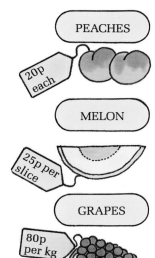

PEACHES
20p each

MELON
25p per slice

GRAPES
80p per kg

95

1 Divide the abacus number on the right by 10 and write
  the answer in digits.
2 Find the total of 300, 10 000 and 70.
3 What is the product of the even numbers greater than 9
  and less than 13?
4 What is the missing number in this subtraction?
5 There are 90 boys and 110 girls at Lakeside
  School. Three-quarters are under 10 years of age.
  How many are 10 or over?
6 Cycling proficiency tests were held in a large school
  of 500 pupils. Half the pupils were tested and only 60 failed.
  How many passed the test?

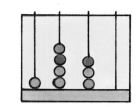

$$\begin{array}{r} 9\ 0\ 0 \\ -\ \blacksquare\ \blacksquare\ \blacksquare \\ \hline 4\ 0\ 5 \end{array}$$

Sold by a shop

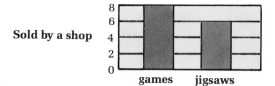

games   jigsaws

7 The games are worth £2·25 each. What is the total value of the games sold?
8 What is the total value of the jigsaws, if they are worth £4·99 each?

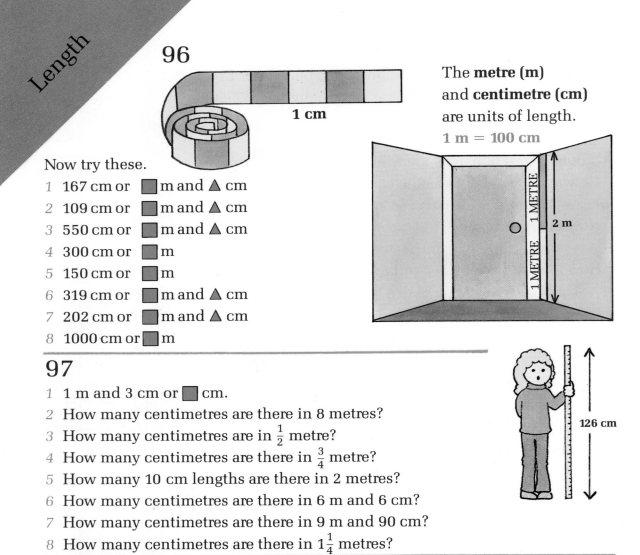

96

1 cm

The **metre (m)** and **centimetre (cm)** are units of length.

1 m = 100 cm

1 METRE

1 METRE

2 m

Now try these.

1 167 cm or ▢ m and ▲ cm
2 109 cm or ▢ m and ▲ cm
3 550 cm or ▢ m and ▲ cm
4 300 cm or ▢ m
5 150 cm or ▢ m
6 319 cm or ▢ m and ▲ cm
7 202 cm or ▢ m and ▲ cm
8 1000 cm or ▢ m

97

1 1 m and 3 cm or ▢ cm.
2 How many centimetres are there in 8 metres?
3 How many centimetres are in $\frac{1}{2}$ metre?
4 How many centimetres are there in $\frac{3}{4}$ metre?
5 How many 10 cm lengths are there in 2 metres?
6 How many centimetres are there in 6 m and 6 cm?
7 How many centimetres are there in 9 m and 90 cm?
8 How many centimetres are there in $1\frac{1}{4}$ metres?

126 cm

98   Very small measurements are made in **millimetres.**

Here is part of a ruler marked off in centimetres and millimetres.

1 How many millimetres are there in 9 cm?
2 How many millimetres are there in 4 cm?

3 How many millimetres are there in $5\frac{1}{2}$ cm?

4 How many millimetres are there in 73 cm?

5 63 mm = ⬜ cm and ▲ mm

6 290 mm = ⬜ cm

7 15 mm = ⬜ cm

8 How many millimetres are there in half a metre?

99

We can think of one metre in any of these ways:

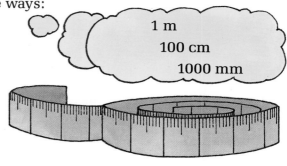

1 m
100 cm
1000 mm

1 2 metres = ⬜ cm or ▲ mm

2 7 metres = ⬜ cm or ▲ mm

3 9000 mm = ⬜ cm or ▲ m

4 6000 mm = ⬜ cm or ▲ m

5 3500 mm = ⬜ cm or ▲ m and ⬜ mm

6 6200 mm = ⬜ cm or ▲ m and ⬜ mm

7 5 m and 400 mm = ⬜ mm

8 3 m and 30 mm = ⬜ mm

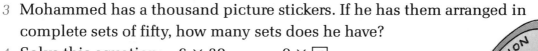

100

1 Write eighteen thousand and eighteen in digits.

2 Subtract five hundred and five from this calculator number.

3 Mohammed has a thousand picture stickers. If he has them arranged in complete sets of fifty, how many sets does he have?

4 Solve this equation: $6 \times 30 = 9 \times \boxed{n}$

5 Write the correct symbol (>, < or =) in place of ⬤.
    88 × 9 ⬤ 8 × 99

6 Mark has saved 95p towards this Frisbee. How much more does he need?

7 Usha bought 4 notebooks for £1·04. How much were they each?

8 I have £0·35 made up of an equal number of twos and fives.
   How many coins do I have altogether?

£2·05

101

1 60 cm + 80 cm + 40 cm = ▢ m ▲ cm

2 6 m + 4 m 18 cm = ▢ m ▲ cm

3 $3\frac{1}{2}$ m + 7 m 20 cm = ▢ m ▲ cm

4 2 m 20 cm + 6 m 90 cm = ▢ m ▲ cm

5 95 cm + 4 m 15 cm = ▢ m ▲ cm

6 3 m 80 cm + 5 m 80 cm = ▢ m ▲ cm

7 1 cm 9 mm + 8 mm = ▢ cm ▲ mm

8 4 cm 7 mm + 43 mm = ▢ cm

102

1 1 m − 73 cm = ▢ cm

2 3 m − 1 m 30 cm = ▢ m ▲ cm

3 4 m 20 cm − 90 cm = ▢ m ▲ cm

4 6 m 50 cm − 3 m 80 cm = ▢ m ▲ cm

5 $1\frac{3}{4}$ m − 70 cm = ▢ m ▲ cm

6 3 cm − 1 cm 6 mm = ▢ cm ▲ mm

7 4 cm 3 mm − 1 cm 5 mm = ▢ cm ▲ mm

8 2 cm 6 mm − 16 mm = ▢ cm

103

Metres and centimetres are like pounds and pence.

£1·00 = 100p £2·37 means 2 pounds 37 pence. The point separates the pounds from the pence.	1·00 m = 100 cm 2·37 m means 2 metres 37 centimetres. The point separates the metres from the centimetres.

Write these in full.

1 a £0·09 = ▢ pence
  b 0·09 m = ▢ centimetres

2 a £5·00 = ▢ pence
  b 5·00 m = ▢ cm

3 a £6·37 = ▢ pence
  b 6·37 m = ▢ cm

4 a £9·43 = ▢ pounds ▲ pence
  b 9·43 m = ▢ m ▲ cm

5 a 380 cm = ▢ m ▲ cm
  b 380 cm = ▢ m

6 a 436 cm = ▢ m ▲ cm
  b 436 cm = ▢ m

7 a 103 cm = ▢ m ▲ cm
  b 103 cm = ▢ m

8 a 7·65 m = ▢ m ▲ cm
  b 7·65 m = ▢ cm

104

Find the cost of:

1 1·50 m at 8p a metre.
2 150 cm at 80p a metre.
3 1·25 m at 16p a metre.
4 20 cm at 40p a metre.
5 37 cm at £1 a metre.
6 1 m and 45 cm at £1 a metre.
7 1·10 m at £1 a metre.
8 250 cm at £4 a metre.

105

1 Each of these tubes holds two hundred chocolate beans. How many beans are there altogether? Write the answer in digits.
2 40 000 + 1400 = 30 000 + ▨
3 69 + 40 + 200 = 209 + ▨
4 Find the sum of the product of 8 and 7 and the product of 4 and 11.
5 $\frac{48}{6}+\frac{14}{7}+\frac{5}{5}$ = ▨
6 (9 × 17) + 17 = ▨
7 Usha gave 3 fifties for 3 batteries costing 35p each. How much change did she receive?
8 What fraction of the number of shapes are the triangles?

106

Greatest distances are measured in **kilometres (km)**.
1 km = 1000 m

1 4 km = ▨ m
2 7 km = ▨ m
3 15 km = ▨ m
4 $9\frac{1}{2}$ km = ▨ m
5 13 000 m = ▨ km
6 4000 m = ▨ km
7 25 000 m = ▨ km
8 10 250 m = ▨ km

19 km

NICE

107

Complete these statements, like this:

1400 m = 1 km and 400 m.

1 6700 m = ■ km and ▲ m   2 7420 m = ■ km and ▲ m

3 6060 m = ■ km and ▲ m   4 10 500 m = ■ km

5 4 km and 700 m = ■ m   6 10 km and 10 m = ■ m

7 14 km and 4 m = ■ m   8 $\frac{3}{4}$ kilometre = ■ m

108

1 How many metres less than a kilometre are 630m?

2 How many metres less than a kilometre are 905 m?

3 350 m + ■ m = 2 km

4 What is the distance from Linton to Dimley?

5 Yusaf visited his cousin's home, a distance of 4 km.
   If he cycled 1200 m, how many metres did he walk?

6 Mira lives a distance of 750 metres from her school.
   If she walked to and from school twice a day, what
   distance in kilometres did she walk?

DIMLEY 83 km

LINTON 37 km

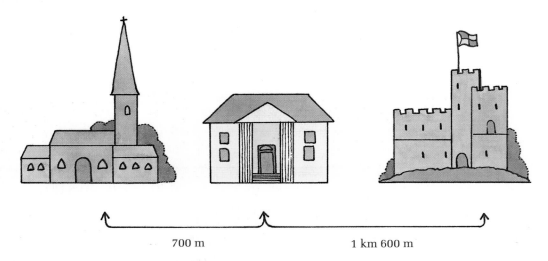

700 m   1 km 600 m

7 What is the distance from the church to the castle?

8 How many metres more is it from the town hall to
   the castle than from the town hall to the church?

109

1 What is the distance from Napley to Datchton?
2 What is the distance from Loxham to Lea?
3 The distance from Datchton to Gaton is 7 km.
   What is the distance from Datchton to Loxham?
4 If a cyclist has covered 1500 m travelling from Gaton to Lea,
   how much further has he to cycle?
5 I walked from Napley to Radnor and back. How far did I walk?
6 What is the shortest distance from Dinton to Slapton?

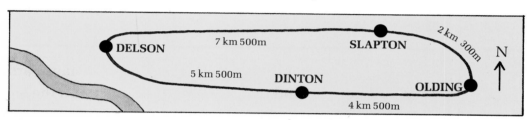

7 What is the distance from Olding through Dinton to Delson?
8 What is the distance from Delson through Slapton and Olding to Dinton?

110

1 Each of these boys was given 50 marbles.
   How many marbles were given out altogether?
2 How many fives are equal in value to 7 fifties?
3 Solve this equation: 130 = (**n** times 11) + 9.
4 4085 + 915 = ▨
5 Work out the score on the bagatelle board on the right.
6 A surveying tape is 20 metres long. How many centimetres is this?

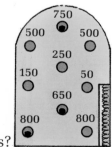

7

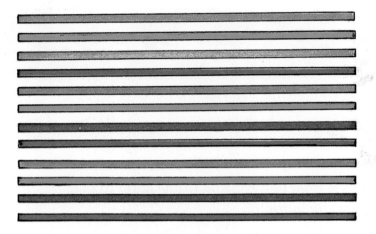

Each of these rods measures 9 cm. What is the total
length in m and cm of the rods?

8 $800 \text{ m} + \boxed{} \text{ m} = 1\frac{1}{2} \text{ km}$

111

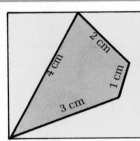

The **perimeter** of a shape is the **distance around** it.
To find the perimeter of the shape on the left we add
the lengths of the sides.

$$2 \text{ cm} + 1 \text{ cm} + 3 \text{ cm} + 4 \text{ cm} = 10 \text{ cm}$$

The **perimeter** is 10 cm

Use your ruler to find the perimeter of each shape below.

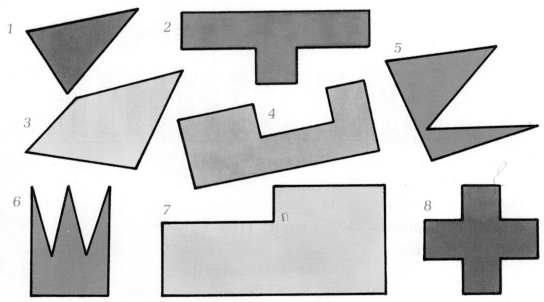

112

The perimeter of Ann's rabbit run is
8 m + 12 m + 13 m + 17 m = 50 m.

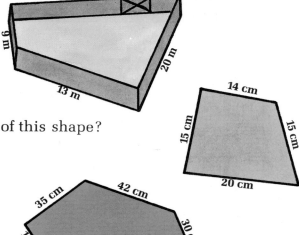

1 Work out the length of
   fencing needed for this garden.
   27 m + 20 m + 9 m + 13 m
       = ▮ m

2 What is the total length of the sides of this shape?

3 Work out the perimeter of
   this shape in m and cm.

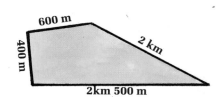

4 What is the distance
   round this park?

5 What is the perimeter of a field with sides of 310 m, 190 m, 70 m and 30 m?
6 Work out the perimeter in m and cm of a piece of cardboard
   with sides of 7 cm, 17 cm 30 cm and 83 cm.
7 Find the perimeter of a garden with sides of 75 m, 42 m, 58 m, and 10 m.
8 Find the perimeter of a triangular piece of cardboard with sides of
   1 m and 10 cm, 1 m and 65 cm, and 1 m and 25 cm.

113

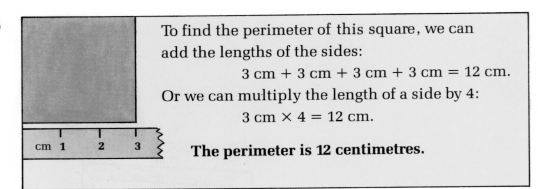

To find the perimeter of this square, we can add the lengths of the sides:

$$3 \text{ cm} + 3 \text{ cm} + 3 \text{ cm} + 3 \text{ cm} = 12 \text{ cm}.$$

Or we can multiply the length of a side by 4:

$$3 \text{ cm} \times 4 = 12 \text{ cm}.$$

The perimeter is 12 centimetres.

1 Find the perimeter of this triangle.

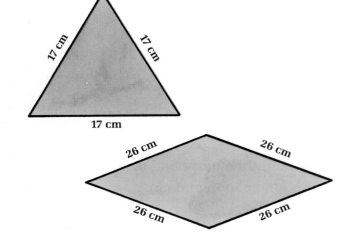

2 Find the perimeter of this shape.

3 Find the perimeter of this shape.

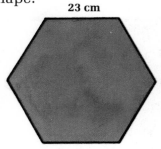

4 Find the perimeter of this square in m and cm.

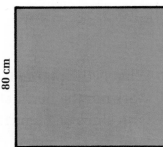

5 The perimeter of a square is 1 m and 20 cm. What is the length of a side?

6 The perimeter of a square piece of card is 1 m and 60 cm. What is the length of a side?

7 Find the perimeter of
this shape.

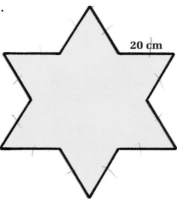

20 cm

8 Find the length of one
side of this triangular
garden, if its perimeter
is 450 m.

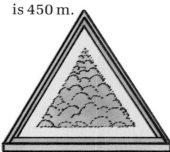

114

1 How many times would you have to run
around the field on the right
to run a kilometre?

50 m

200 m

100 m

150 m

2 The length of edging needed to go round a square table top
is 2 m 80 cm. What is the length of a side?

3 A toy racing car covers 2 m and 40 cm during one circuit
of the inside track and 3 m and 20 cm during a circuit of
the outside track. What is the difference in centimetres?

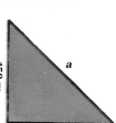

4 A runner did three laps of a running track and covered 1 km and 200 m.
What was the distance round the track?

5 One circuit of a model railway track is 3 m and 50 cm.
What distance would be covered by a train that did ten circuits.

6 A triangle has two sides of 70 cm and one side of
60 cm. What is its perimeter in metres?

7 A field has sides of 70 m, 40 m, 60 m and 30 m.
What is its perimeter?

8 The perimeter of the field is $\frac{1}{2}$ km.
What is the length of the side marked a?

150 m

a

150 m

115

1 Find half of seven thousand and seventy and write the answer in digits.

2 Write a multiplication equation for this addition and put the product in place of **n**.
$$9 + 9 + 9 + 9 + 9 + 9 + 9 + 9 + 9 = n$$

3 Write the correct sign (>, < or =) in place of ⬤.
$$(2 \times 7) + (7 \times 8) \ ⬤ \ 70$$

4 $47 + 9 + 33 = $ ▣

5 What are the missing digits in this addition?

▣▣
$$\underline{+ \ 7 \ 6}$$
$$1 \ 2 \ 0$$

10 cm

6 £9·70 − £0·97 = £ ▣

7 Work out the perimeter in cm of the star on the right.

8 340 m + ▣ m = 1 km and 40 m

116

Two units of weight in the metric system are the **gram (g)** and the **kilogram (kg)**.

1 kg = 1000 g

This chicken weighs 1300 grams.

What is the total in grams of each of these collections of weights?

1

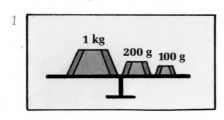

2

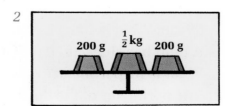

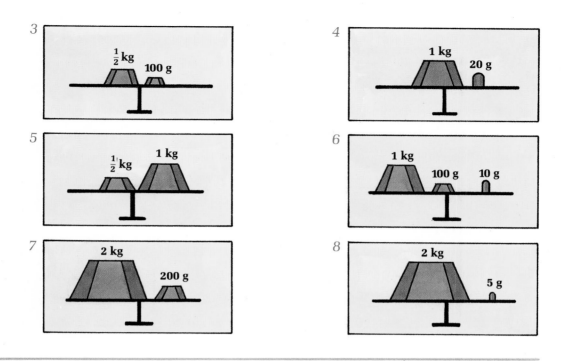

117

Give the weight shown on each scale. Each division on a scale stands for 100 g.

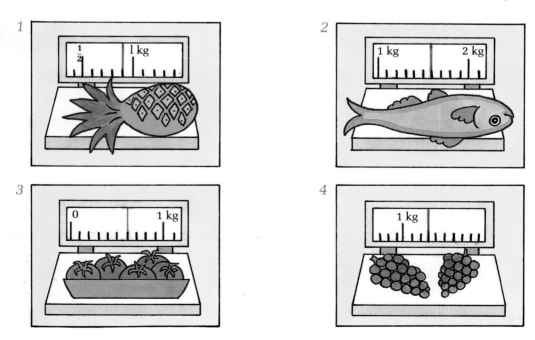

What is the weight of each packet?

5

6
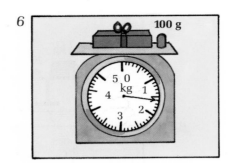

7

8

118

What is the weight in grams shown by the pointer at:

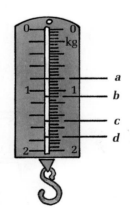

1 *a*?

2 *b*?

3 *c*?

4 *d*?

5 1900 g = ▉ kg and ▲ g

6 5005 g = ▉ kg and ▲ g

7 7070 g = ▉ kg and ▲ g

8 6808 g = ▉ kg and ▲ g

119

10 grams   50 grams   100 grams   200 grams   500 grams

Which of the weights would you use to weigh these?

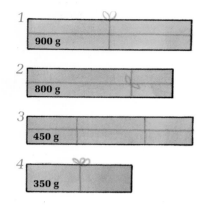

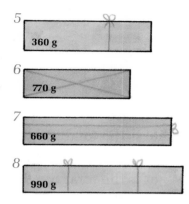

120

1 Complete the sentence below.

Ten thousand is ■ hundreds.

2 How many dozen eggs are there in 6 trays, if each tray holds 48 eggs?

3 Solve this equation: $(7 \times 8) + \boxed{r} = 59$.

4 Sue, Ann and Jane had 42 pearls. They made them into three bracelets of the same size. How many pearls were in each bracelet?

5 Write the number which can be written in place of ■.

$3840 \div \blacksquare = 38 \text{ r } 40$

6 What change would you receive from £5 after spending £0·72 and £0·78?

7 4 fifties + 4 tens + ■ pennies = £2·45

8 What length of tape is needed to frame the new class notice board?

121

What number can we write in place of each ■?

1 $230 \text{ g} + \blacksquare \text{ g} = \frac{1}{2} \text{ kg}$ 2 $490 \text{ g} + \blacksquare \text{ g} = 1 \text{ kg}$

3 $900 \text{ g} + \blacksquare \text{ g} = 3 \text{ kg}$ 4 $100 \text{ g} + \blacksquare \text{ g} = \frac{1}{4} \text{ kg}$

5 $4 \text{ kg} - 3100 \text{ g} = \blacksquare \text{ g}$ 6 $3 \text{ kg} - \frac{1}{4} \text{ kg} = \blacksquare \text{ g}$

7 $1 \text{ kg and } 700 \text{ g} - 900 \text{ g} = \blacksquare \text{ g}$

8 $7 \text{ kg} - 700 \text{ g} = \blacksquare \text{ g}$

122

1 What is the total weight in kg and g of the pot of jam and packet of butter?
2 What is the total weight of the salt and the salmon?
3 What is the total weight of the peas, sardines and oats?
4 What is the total weight of 2 jars of jam?
5 What is the total weight of 5 tins of salmon?
6 $900 \text{ g} + 400 \text{ g} + 600 \text{ g} + 100 \text{ g} = \blacksquare \text{ kg}$
7 $1 \text{ kg and } 600 \text{ g} + 2 \text{ kg and } 800 \text{ g} = \blacksquare \text{ kg} \blacktriangle \text{ g}$
8 What is the total weight of the salt and the butter?

123

1 Take 800 g from $1\frac{1}{2}$ kg.
2 Subtract 900 g from 2 kg.
3 Find the difference between 1 kg 700 g and 5 kg.
4 How many grams are left when 3 kg and 30 g are taken from 5 kg?
5 How many grams must be added to 6 kg 600 g to make 10 kg?
6 What is the difference in kg and g between 7 kilograms and 700 grams.
7 $4 \text{ kg and } 400 \text{ g} - 1 \text{ kg and } 500 \text{ g} = \blacksquare \text{ kg} \blacktriangle \text{ g}$
8 What is the weight in kg and g of this parcel?

124

Work out the costs of these.
1 1500 grams at 8p per kg
2 3 kg 500 g at 12p per kg
3 1 kg 250 g at 16p per kg
4 750 g at 12p per kg
5 200 g at 20p per kg
6 300 g at £10 per kg
7 900 g at £1·00 per kg
8 2 kg 100 g at 10p per kg

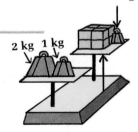

200 g

2 kg 1 kg

125

1 By how many would this abacus be increased if I moved the 3 beads from the units column to the thousands column?
2 Solve this equation: $450 + 300 = 1000 - \boxed{n}$.
3 Write the correct sign (= or ≠) in place of ⬤.
   $4 \times 7 + 4 \ ⬤ \ 5 \times 7$
4 How many rounders balls costing 60p each could you buy with £6·60?
5 Three packages together weigh 2 kg. The first weighs 800 g and the second 900 g. What is the weight of the other package?
6 How many metres are there in 10 km and 10 m?
7 What is the weight of the box and the apples?

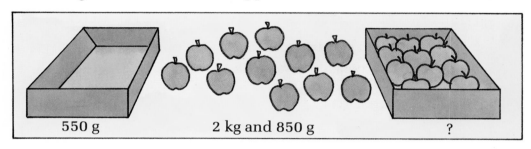

550 g   2 kg and 850 g   ?

8 What is the perimeter in metres of this square garden?

19 m

126

1 Each box is the same weight. What is the total weight in kg and g of all the boxes?
2 These lollipops together weigh 1 kg. What is the weight of one?

3 Find $\frac{1}{3}$ of the difference between 1 kg 600 g and 700 g?
4 What is the weight in kg and g of the four tins?

430g   430g   430g   430g

5 How many 20 gram weights are needed to balance $\frac{1}{2}$ kilogram?
6 What is the total weight in kilograms of 12 fruit cakes, each weighing 1250 g.
7 Ten toffees weigh 125 g. How many are there in a box holding a kilogram?
8 What is the average weight of an orange?

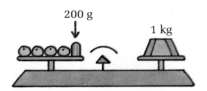

200 g   1 kg

127

The **litre** is the basic unit of liquid measure. We write ℓ for litre.
The **millilitre** is used to measure small amounts of liquid. We write **ml** for millilitre.
A medicine spoon holds about 5 millilitres.

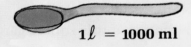

1ℓ = 1000 ml

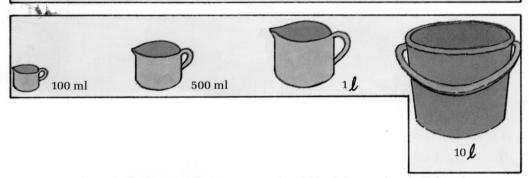

100 ml   500 ml   1ℓ

10ℓ

1 How many times can the 500 ml container be filled from the full bucket?
2 How many times can the 100 ml container be filled from the litre container?
3 About how many medicine spoons can be filled from $\frac{1}{4}\ell$?
4 How many times can the 100 ml container be filled from the full bucket?
5 How many millilitres are there in $\frac{3}{4}$ litre?
6 How many 500 ml bottles can be filled from 12 litres?
7 How many 300 ml bottles can be filled from 3 litres?
8 How many 40 ml bottles can be filled from 4 litres?

73

128

| 3 ℓ and 300 ml = 3300 ml |

Complete these statements.

1 4 ℓ and 40 ml = ◼ ml
2 6 ℓ and 750 ml = ◼ ml
3 2 ℓ and 7 ml = ◼ ml
4 1 ℓ and 36 ml = ◼ ml
5 4080 ml = ◼ ℓ and ▲ ml
6 1700 ml = ◼ ℓ and ▲ ml
7 6007 ml = ◼ ℓ and ▲ ml
8 2027 ml = ◼ ℓ and ▲ ml

129

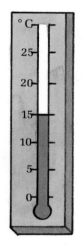

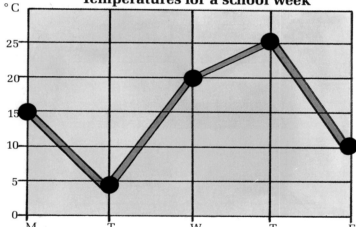

Temperatures for a school week

1 What is the highest recorded temperature?
2 What is the difference between the highest and lowest temperature?
3 What is the average of the recorded temperatures?
4 On how many days was the temperature above 15° C?
5 On which day was the temperature 20° higher than on Tuesday?
6 What is the difference between the temperatures on Monday and Friday?
7 If the temperature shown on the thermometer dropped 20° then rose 12°, what would the temperature be?
8 The temperature was 5° C. It rose 9°, then fell 7°. What was it then?

130

1 Find half of ninety thousand and write the answer in digits.

2 Solve this equation: $5000 - \boxed{a} = 50$.

3 $5 \times 7 \times 9 \times 2 \times 1 = \blacksquare$

4 What number can be written in place of ▪▪
in this multiplication example?

$$\begin{array}{r} \blacksquare\,\blacksquare \\ \times\ 7 \\ \hline 1\ \ 0\ \ 5 \end{array}$$

5 Work out the cost of a hundred crayons at 10p each.

6 Claire has to walk $1\frac{1}{2}$ km to school. After
walking 600 m, she called at the library.
How far did she still have to walk?

7 What fraction of these eggs is brown?

1 DOZEN EGGS

8

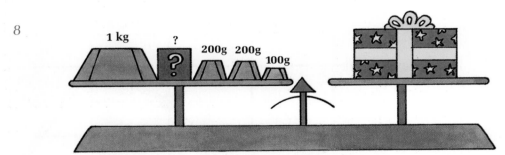

1 kg   ?   200g 200g   100g

The parcel weighs 2 kg. What is the hidden weight?

131

The time shown by clock (a)
can be written in two ways:

12.10 or **10 past 12.**

(a)

The time shown by clock (b)
can be written in two ways:

10.40 or **20 to 11.**

(b)

Write these times the short way, for example 12.10.

 1   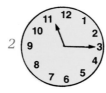 2    3   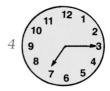 4

Write these times the long way, for example 10 past 12.

 5    6    7   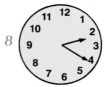 8

132

> On some timetables, twenty minutes past three in the morning is written **3.20 am** and twenty minutes past three in the afternoon is written **3.20 pm**.
> Ten minutes to nine in the morning is written **8.50 am** and ten minutes to nine in the evening is written **8.50 pm**.

Write these times in the same way.

1   ten minutes past ten in the morning

2   ten minutes to ten in the evening

3   a quarter to three in the afternoon

4   twenty-five minutes to nine in the morning

5   Write in words 7.45 pm.

6   Write in words 2.19 am.

7   Write in words 11.30 pm.

8   Write in words 7.27 am.

133

> **1 hour (h) = 60 minutes (min).**
> **1 minute = 60 seconds (s).**

1   3 minutes (min) = ☐ seconds (s)   2   10 mins = ☐ s

3   1 min 29 s = ☐ s   4   4 min 13 s = ☐ s

5   83 s = ☐ min ▲ s   6   300 s = ☐ min

7   $2\frac{1}{2}$ min = ☐ s   8 $1\frac{1}{4}$ min = ☐ s

134

1 How many minutes are there in 1 hour 37 minutes?
2 Change 100 minutes to hours and minutes.
3 How many hours are there in 600 minutes?
4 How many minutes are there in one-third of an hour?
5 How many minutes are there in $1\frac{3}{4}$ hours?
6 3 hours 20 minutes = ■ min
7 150 min = ■ h ▲ min
8 5 h 30 min = ■ min

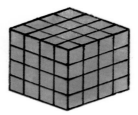

135

1 How many small cubes 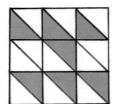 are there in the large cube?
2 $37 \times 5 = (30 \times 5) + (■ \times 5)$
3 Subtract 100 from 8080.
4 What change should you receive from £10·00 after spending £1·10?
5 Solve this equation: $45 + 47 = \boxed{x} + 25$.
6 What fraction of the square on the right is coloured.
7 How many $\frac{1}{2}$ kg are there in 3500 grams?
8 A car uses an average of 10 ℓ of petrol every 90 km.
How much petrol would it use on a journey of 270 km?

136

Between 1.35
and 2.10
there are 35 minutes.

How many minutes are there between:

1 4.20 and 5.00?
2 1.15 and 2.10?
3 3.17 and 4.00?
4 6.45 and 7.20?
5 2.50 and 3.10?
6 5.27 and 6.05?
7 4.40 and 5.30?
8 8.53 and 9.47?

137 Railway, bus and airline timetables use the **24-hour clock.**

	LONDON	EDINBURGH
	Depart	Arrive
	08 00	12 54
	09 00	13 53
	10 00	15 40
	10 35	15 09
	11 00	15 50
	12 00	16 44
	13 00	17 50
	14 00	18 44
	15 00	19 47
	16 00	20 44
	17 00	21 52
	22 50	05 28
	23 20	07 00

The Flying Scotsman leaves London at 10 35.
The journey to Edinburgh takes **4 hours 34 minutes**.
Use the timetable to work out in hours and minutes
the time taken by the trains which leave London
at these times.

1 08 00   2 10 00   3 13 00   4 15 00
5 16 00   6 17 00   7 22 50   8 23 20

138

These clocks are 20 minutes fast. What is the correct time?

1    2

These 24-hour digital clocks are 25 minutes slow.
What is the correct time?

3    4

These clocks are 35 minutes fast. What is the correct time?

5    6

These clocks are 40 minutes slow. What is the correct time?

7 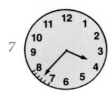   8

139

The time twenty minutes after 8.55 is **9.15.**

1 What is the time fifteen minutes before 9.05?
2 What is the time half an hour after 3.33?
3 What is the time twenty-five minutes before 9.15?
4 What is the time three-quarters of an hour before 8.30?
5 What is the time ten minutes before 3.07?
6 What is the time forty minutes after 7.30?
7 What is the time fifty-five minutes before 6.15?
8 What is the time ten minutes before 12.05 pm?

140

1 How many small cubes 🔲 are there in the picture below?

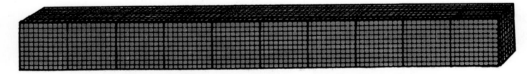

2 Find the number which can be placed instead of ■.
        7006 = ■ + 16
3 Solve this equation: $6 \times \boxed{r} \times 3 = 72$.
4 What change would I have from £5 after spending
   £1·85 and £0·65?
5 A bank changed £10 into 10p pieces. How many
   coins were there?
6 What is the total weight in kilograms of the packets
   of butter?

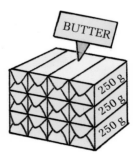

7 How many millimetres are there in $7\frac{1}{2}$ centimetres?

8 How many 10 ml containers can be filled from 2 litres of perfume?

141

The timetable time for one minute before midnight is 2359.

Give timetable times for these.

1 ten minutes to midday

2 twenty minutes after noon

3 two and a half hours after 11.00 am

4 one and a quarter hours after 3.00 am

5 seven hours after 6.00 pm

6 two and half hours before 1.30 pm

7 one and three-quarter hours before 10.00 am .

8 twenty-five minutes after 11.50 am

142

You can use the calendar to help you with some of these questions.

Do not count the first day
unless the dates are
inclusive.

How many days are there
from:

1 15th January to 4th
February?

2 16th February to 1st
March (not Leap Year)?

3 17th April to 9th May?

4 14th May to 6th June?

5 15th June to 7th
September?

6 17th September to 5th
November (inclusive)?

7 11th December to 10th
February (inclusive)?

8 10th February to 10th March (Leap Year)?

Calendar

	January	February	March
Sun	6 13 20 27	3 10 17 24	3 10 17 24 31
Mon	7 14 21 28	4 11 18 25	4 11 18 25
Tue	1 8 15 22 29	5 12 19 26	5 12 19 26
Wed	2 9 16 23 30	6 13 20 27	6 13 20 27
Thu	3 10 17 24 31	7 14 21 28	7 14 21 28
Fri	4 11 18 25	1 8 15 22	1 8 15 22 29
Sat	5 12 19 26	2 9 16 23	2 9 16 23 30

	April	May	June
Sun	7 14 21 28	5 12 19 26	2 9 16 23 30
Mon	1 8 15 22 29	6 13 20 27	3 10 17 24
Tue	2 9 16 23 30	7 14 21 28	4 11 18 25
Wed	3 10 17 24	1 8 15 22 29	5 12 19 26
Thu	4 11 18 25	2 9 16 23 30	6 13 20 27
Fri	5 12 19 26	3 10 17 24 31	7 14 21 28
Sat	6 13 20 27	4 11 18 25	1 8 15 22 29

	July	August	September
Sun	7 14 21 28	4 11 18 25	1 8 15 22 29
Mon	1 8 15 22 29	5 12 19 26	2 9 16 23 30
Tue	2 9 16 23 30	6 13 20 27	3 10 17 24
Wed	3 10 17 24 31	7 14 21 28	4 11 18 25
Thu	4 11 18 25	1 8 15 22 29	5 12 19 26
Fri	5 12 19 26	2 9 16 23 30	6 13 20 27
Sat	6 13 20 27	3 10 17 24 31	7 14 21 28

	October	November	December
Sun	6 13 20 27	3 10 17 24	1 8 15 22 29
Mon	7 14 21 28	4 11 18 25	2 9 16 23 30
Tue	1 8 15 22 29	5 12 19 26	3 10 17 24 31
Wed	2 9 16 23 30	6 13 20 27	4 11 18 25
Thu	3 10 17 24 31	7 14 21 28	5 12 19 26
Fri	4 11 18 25	1 8 15 22 29	6 13 20 27
Sat	5 12 19 26	2 9 16 23 30	7 14 21 28

143

1 Look at the calendar on the right. What was the date of the Thursday before 2nd January?

2 Look at the calendar. What is the date of the fourth Saturday in January?

3 27th May was a Monday. What day of the week was the last day of May?

4 Karen's birthday was on Tuesday, 31st December, but the party was the following Sunday. What date was that?

5 Work out the date of the first Saturday in September, if 30th August was a Monday.

6 27th September was a Tuesday. What was the date of the next Saturday?

7 17th October was a Friday. What day of the week was 30th October?

8 We broke up for the Whitsun holiday on Friday, 1st June, and returned on 12th June. What day of the week was that?

January				
Sun		6	13 20 27
Mon		7	14 21 28
Tue	1	8	15 22 29
Wed	2	9	16 23 30
Thu	3	10	17 24 31
Fri	4	11	18 25
Sat	5	12	19 26

144

How many:

HOW MANY?

1 months are there with 31 days?

2 hours are there in one week?

3 seconds are there in one hour?

4 days are there in a year when February has 29 days?

5 days are there altogether in April, June, September and November?

6 calendar months are there in 3 years?

7 weeks are there in a year?

8 hours are there from 6.30 pm Monday to 11.30 pm Tuesday?

145

1 A school received three large crates of soap.
Each crate held 100 boxes and each box contained 8 tablets.
How many tablets of soap were there?

2 Write this addition, putting in the missing digits.

$$
\begin{array}{r}
7\ \blacksquare\ 2 \\
+\ \blacksquare\ 7\ 0 \\
\hline
9\ 3\ 2
\end{array}
$$

3 Write this number in our numerals: LXIX

4 What is the distance by plane from New York to London?

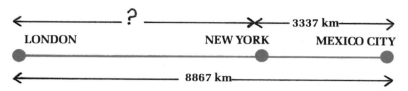

5 Find Ravi's average cricket score.

Game 1	Game 2	Game 3
7	11	6

6 Complete this statement by writing the missing unit.

7 mm × 100 = 70 ▭

7 620 mm + 300 mm + 280 mm = ■ m and ▲ mm.

8 Round off 4390 grams to the nearest kilogram.

146

In one hour this plane flies a distance of 1600 km.
1600 km per hour
1600 km/h

In one hour this car travels a distance of 80 km.
80 km per hour
80 km/h

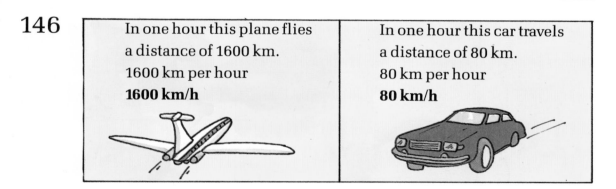

Find the **time**, **speed** or **distance** in each of these problems.

1

100 km

25 km/h

time?

2

180 km

speed?

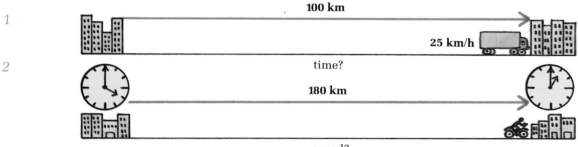

3

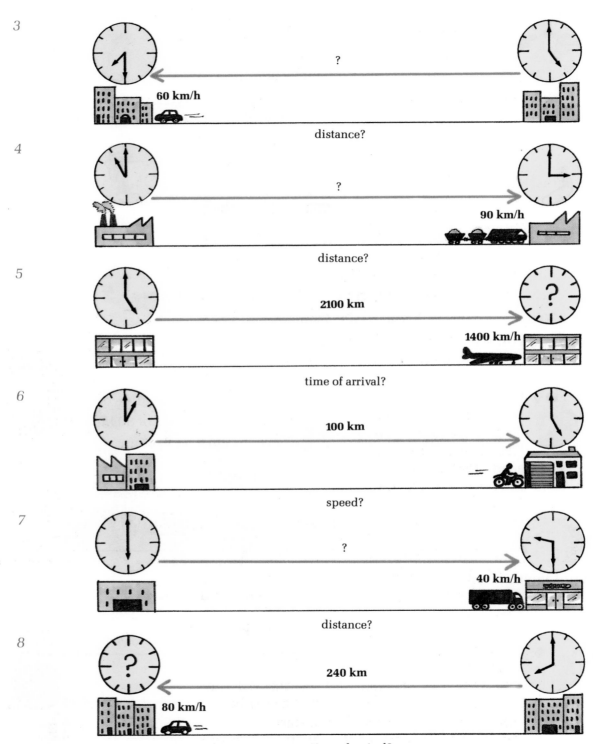

?

60 km/h

distance?

4

?

90 km/h

distance?

5

2100 km

1400 km/h

time of arrival?

6

100 km

speed?

7

?

40 km/h

distance?

8

240 km

80 km/h

time of arrival?

147

1 An aircraft flew at an average speed of 2000 km/h.
   How far did the aircraft fly in 5 hours?

2 A cyclist travelled a distance of 60 km in 4 hours.
   What was her average speed in km/h?

3 What was the distance covered by a motorist who travelled
   at an average speed of 50 km/h for $2\frac{1}{2}$ hours?

4 A man walked from 8.30 am to midday at a steady
   6 km/h. How far did he walk?

5 A coach travelled at an average speed of 50 km/h
   for $3\frac{1}{2}$ hours. How far did it travel?

6 Simon cycled at an average speed of 15 km/h from 10.00 am
   to 11.30 am. How far did he cycle?

7 An aircraft left Heathrow Airport at 10.00 am and reached
   its destination at 2.00 pm. If the distance covered was
   4800 km, what was the average speed of the aircraft?

8 What speed in metres per minute is 5 km in 10 minutes?

CAEN
15 km

148

1 A lorry travelled at a steady speed of 45 km/h.
   How long did it take to reach Caen?

2 How long does a car take to travel 70 km
   at a speed of 60 km/h?

3 A cyclist travelled at a steady speed
   of 20 km/h.
   How long did she take to travel 70 km?

4 **Distance:**   6000 km
       Speed: 1200 km/h
   Time of flight: ? hours

5 A racing cyclist travelled 40 km at an average speed of 30 km/h.
   How long did he take?

6 A coach left at 9 o'clock on a journey of 200 km.
   If it travelled at an average speed of 50 km/h,
   what time did it arrive?

7 Paul cycled to his aunt's home, a distance of 35 km,
   and arrived at 2.45 pm. If he cycled at a steady
   speed of 20 km/h, what time did he start?

8 How long will a car take to reach Calais, if it travels at an
   average speed of 70 km/h?

CALAIS
280 km

149

1 Take two thousand and twenty from 222 222.
2 Write the correct symbol (>, < or =) in place of ●.

$$19\ 590\ ●\ 10\ 000 + 900 + 50$$

3 A pencil costs 18p and a rubber costs 32p.
How much will 5 pencils and 5 rubbers cost?
4 Solve this equation: $\frac{750}{3} + \boxed{n} = 1000$.
5 A school paid £3·50 for ten rulers. What was the cost of one?
6 I have £1·20 made up of an equal number of twos and tens.
How many coins do I have?
7 Julie's medicine bottle held 100 ml. She took 4 doses, each of
5 ml, every day. How long did her medicine last?
8 What is the weight in grams of the package on the scales
on the right?

150

1 Write nine hundred thousand and ninety in digits.
2 $9000 + 900 + 1000 + 100 = \blacksquare$
3 How many TV dinners can be bought with £17?

4 How many coins are there in a bag holding £20 worth of twenties?
5 What fraction of the total number of buttons is red?

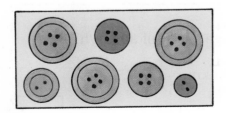

6 $5\ \text{km} - 500\ \text{m} = \blacksquare\ \text{m}$
7 $10\,\ell$ and $10\ \text{ml} = \blacksquare\ \text{ml}$
8 What is the total weight in grams?

151

We have learned that the best unit to use for surface measurement (area) is the square.
The **area** of this shape is **12 square units** when ▢ is the **square unit**.

Count the square units to find the area of these shapes.

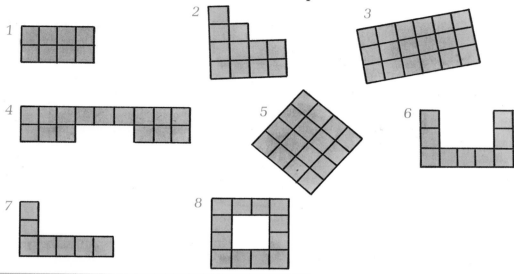

152

In these shapes we can see that there are half squares.
Find the area of each shape.

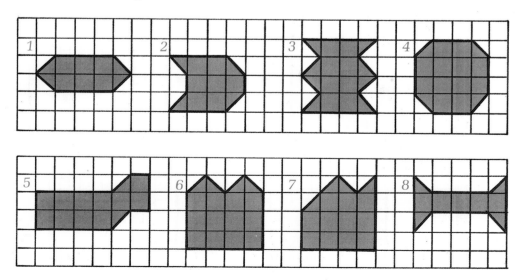

153

Sometimes we have to find the area of curved shapes. To do this we draw the
shape on squared paper, count the number of whole squares, then estimate the
number of squares which should be added.

Try
these.

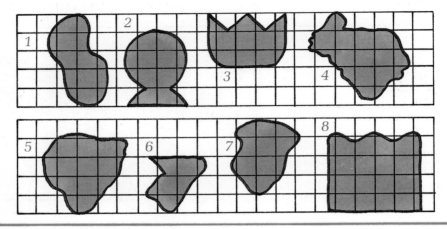

154

We can find the area of rectangles without counting each square.

> There are **7 rows** and there are **4 squares in a row.**
> **(7 × 4) = 28**
> **Area of rectangle is 28 square units.**

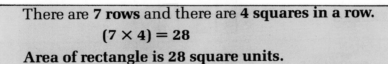

Find the area of each of these rectangles.

This is the square unit used □.

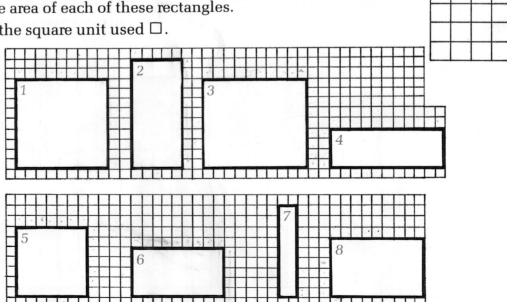

155

 This is a square and each side measures a centimetre.
Its area is **1 square centimetre (cm²).**
This is the unit used for measuring small areas.

The area of this rectangle
can be found by measuring
the length and breadth,
then calculating the area,
like this:

$(5 \times 3) = 15.$

Area is **15 cm².**

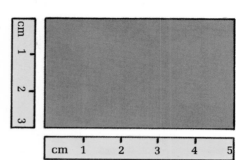

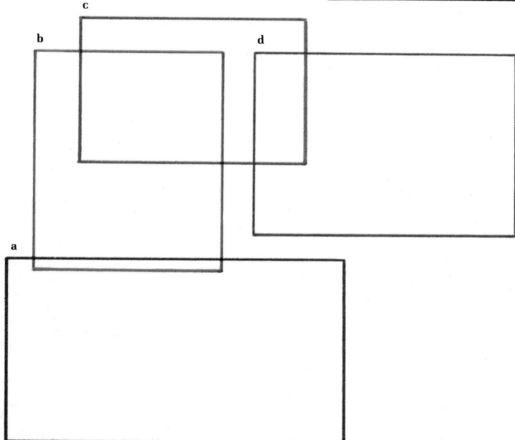

What is the area in cm² of:

1 rectangle **a**?

2 rectangle **c**?

3 rectangle **b**?

4 rectangle **d**?

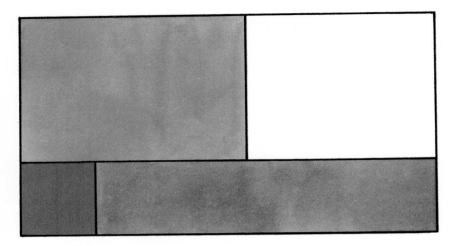

What is the area in cm² of:

5 the brown rectangle?

6 the green rectangle?

7 the red square?

8 the white rectangle?

156

1 A car has travelled 40 700 kilometres. How many kilometres less than fifty thousand is this?

2 5052 means ■ hundreds + 52.

3 $9 \times 8 = (8 \times 3) + (■ \times 8)$

4 The midday temperatures on Monday, Tuesday and Wednesday were 7°C, 9°C and 14°C. Work out the average midday temperature for the three days.

5 Find the cost of 10 number puzzles at 95p each.

6 A coach fare to London is £2·95 and the train fare £3·17. What is the difference in cost?

7 The distance round a square field is 280 metres. What is the length of a side?

8 A car uses 5 litres of petrol every 47 kilometres. How far will it go on 50 litres?

157

1 What is the total distance by air from Oslo to Lisbon then on to Madrid?

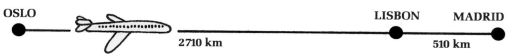

OSLO   LISBON   MADRID

2710 km   510 km

2 Write out the equation, putting in the missing numbers.

$$35 \times 20 = 70 \times \blacksquare = \triangle$$

3 Solve this equation: $54 = (3 \times 9) + (9 \times \boxed{r})$.

4 How many magazines at 60p each can be bought for £12·00?

5 Work out the perimeter of this rectangle.

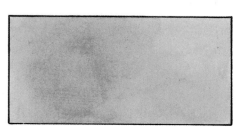

6 Work out the area of this rectangle.

7 A goods train left London at 10 00 for Edinburgh, a distance of 630 km. It arrived in Edinburgh at 17 00. What was its average speed in km/h?

8 What fraction of the picture is coloured?

158

1 Write a Roman numeral for fifty-five.

2 Solve this equation: $\boxed{x} \times 9 = 720$.

3 $(10 \times 1) - (0 \times 10) = \blacksquare$

4 A school bought eight small compasses. What was the total cost?

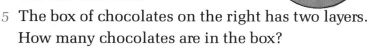

5 The box of chocolates on the right has two layers. How many chocolates are in the box?

6 How much less than £10 is the total of £3·30, £3·50 and £2·10?

7 Mark's pace is 50 cm. How far will he go in 80 paces?

8 These two packages are exactly the same weight. What is the weight in kg and g of each package?

159

1 Subtract a hundred from 3017 and write the answer in digits.

2 What is the missing number in this addition?

$$\begin{array}{r} 2\ 9 \\ +\ \blacksquare\blacksquare \\ \hline 9\ 6 \end{array}$$

3 Two thousand envelopes are put in packs of 25.
How many packs are there?

4 £3·50 − £2·87 = £ ▪

5 1250 g × 12 = ▪ kg

6 20 litres of petrol weigh 15 kg. What is
the weight in grams of a litre?

7 The length of a car is given as 4628 mm. What is
this in metres and millimetres?

8 What is the average of the temperatures shown on the right?

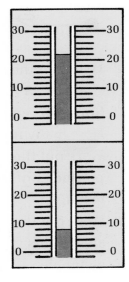

160

1 Round off this number to the nearest thousand:

19 639.

2 Write the correct symbol (>, < or =) in place of ⬤.

209 + 100 ⬤ 98 + 207

3 Six friends shared a box of chocolate drops. They had nine each
and there were four left over. How many were in the full box?

4 What fraction of the square on the right is coloured green?

5 What is the total cost of the dress and shoes?

6 Find the perimeter in cm of a square with sides of 30 mm.

7 How many days are there from 10th January to 23rd February (inclusive)?

8 What is the weight of the cream?

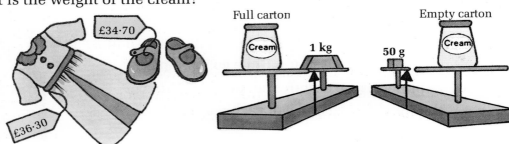

161

1 Add eighty to eight hundred and eight.
2 What is the difference between 10 000 and 10?
3 Find the total of 990, 400 and 10.
4 Subtract 500 from 5050.
5 Write the missing numeral:

   2750, 3500, 4250, [＿＿＿], 5750, 6500
6 100 000 = 500 + 49 500 + [＿＿＿]
7 250 + 678 + 150 = [＿]
8 Solve this equation: 50 − 23 = 100 − n.

162

1 $(23 \times 1) + (23 \times 0) =$ [＿]
2 $9 + 8 + 7 + 6 + 4 + 3 + 2 + 1 =$ [＿]

3 Find one-eleventh of 99 099.
4 $\frac{1}{8}$ of a certain number is 250. What is $\frac{1}{4}$ of that number?
5 $(25 + 25 + 25 + 25) \times 19 =$ [＿]
6 $(12 \times 12) + (24 \times 9) =$ [＿]
7 $(770 + 230) \div 100 =$ [＿]
8 What is $\frac{1}{6}$ of 6216?

163

1 There were 785 people at a circus performance.
   The circus tent has 850 seats. How many seats were empty?
2 Ann made 36 sausage rolls and Jane made 24. At the party,
   how many children could have three each?
3 Peter had 75 picture stickers. He gave a dozen to his brother.
   He then shared the rest equally among nine of his friends.
   How many did each friend get?
4 This building has nine floors and also a basement.
   There is an average of 29 people working on each floor
   and the basement. How many people work in
   the building altogether?

5 Zena has 30 United States stamps and 80 Italian stamps. Salim has 60 foreign stamps. How many more stamps than Salim does Zena have?

6 A class has a stock of 5000 pencils. If 25 pencils are needed each week, how many weeks will the pencils last?

7 A satellite in orbit travels about 8 kilometres per second. About how far will it travel in a minute?

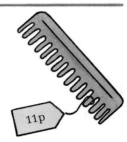

8 An aircraft has already covered a third of its 1200 kilometre flight. What distance has it still to fly?

164

Find the cost of:

1 eleven combs.

2 4 notebooks at 40p each.

3 2 rulers at 65p each.

4 5 rubbers at 33p each.

5 6 ballpoint pens at 99p each.

6 60 crayons at 4p each.

7 50 envelopes at 8p each.

8 20 pencils at 15p each.

55p

11p

165

1 If 5 apples cost 55p, how many can you buy for 99p?

2 If plums are 2 for 7p, how many can you buy for £1·40?

3 If buttons are 7p a dozen, how many can you buy for 70p?

4 If sweets are 5 for 3p, how many can you buy for £3?

5 If pears are 3 for 20p, how much do 30 cost?

6 If peaches are 3 for 50p, how much is a dozen?

7 If gobstoppers are 5 for 9p, how much would 100 cost?

8 If picture stickers are 12 for 10p, how much would you pay for 10 dozen?

166

SALE ⅓ OFF!

Stay Tight

1 How much was paid for a calculator in a sale, if its usual price was £7·50?

2 How many balloons at 4p each can be bought with 6 twenties?

3 How much was paid for all the spanners, if the average price of a spanner was 80p?

4 David bought a pen for £2·45. He gave 11 fives and the rest in tens.
  How many tens did he give?

5 Susan needs £5 for a large jigsaw. She has 6 fifties and 15 tens.
  How much more does she need?

6 300 washers cost £3. How much is each washer worth?

7 How much change is there from £20 after spending £9·10 and £10·09?

8 10 notebooks cost £4. What is the cost of 6 notebooks?

167

Find the cost of:

1 1·50 m of wire.

2 75 cm of wire.

3 1·25 m at 8p per metre.

4 10 cm at £1·50 per metre.

5 93 cm at £1 per metre.

6 120 cm at 50p per metre.

7 2 m and 20 cm at £5 per metre.

8 1·85 m at £1 per metre.

168

1 How many 30 cm lengths can be cut from 3 metres?

2 How many 50 cm lengths can be cut from 9 metres?

3 How many 25 cm lengths can be cut from 20 m?

4 How many 15 cm lengths can be cut from $1\frac{1}{2}$ m?

5 How many 60 cm lengths can be cut from 1 m 80 cm?

6 How many 40 cm lengths can be cut from 4 m?

7 How many pieces, each $4\frac{1}{2}$ cm long, can be cut from 4·5m?

8 A boy's pace is $\frac{3}{4}$ m. How many paces does he take to walk 75 m?

169

side	length
A	23 cm
B	22 cm
C	▣ cm

1 The table on the right shows the lengths of two sides of a triangle. The perimeter of the triangle is 1 metre. What is the length of side **C**?

2 We know that 1 metre = 100 centimetres and 1 kilometre = 1000 metres. How many centimetres are there in ten kilometres?

3 A carpenter made 9 shelves, each 70 cm long. What length of wood in m and cm was used?

4 Find the average in cm of these lengths: $\frac{1}{4}$ m, 35 cm and 300 mm.

5 Three and a half metres of wire was cut into five equal pieces. What was the length in millimetres of each piece?

6 A metal strip is 200 mm long. How many of these strips can be cut from a longer strip 2 m 20 cm in length?

7 Robert's pace is 70 cm. How many metres has he walked after taking 20 paces?

8 Forty centimetres are cut off this ribbon. How many centimetres of ribbon remain on the roll?

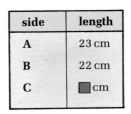

4 m

170

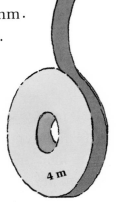

1 kg

1 Each book is the same weight. What is the weight of one book?

2 One litre of oil weighs 910 g. What is the weight in kilograms of 100 litres of oil?

3 What is the cost of 1500 grams at £2·50 per kilogram?

4 A basket of fruit weighs 18 kg 500 g. The empty basket weighs 900 g. What is the weight of the fruit?

5 $10\frac{3}{4}$ kg of coffee was made up into packets of 250 g. How many packets were there?

6 What is the total weight in kilograms of 12 parcels, each weighing 750 grams?

7 Three melons weigh $\frac{1}{2}$ kg, 400 g and 600 g. What is the average weight?

8 Find the total weight of 16 boxes, each weighing 10 kg 500 g.

171

1 Each of the tins in this box holds 250 g of drinking chocolate.
How many kg of drinking chocolate are there in the full box?

2 If 1 kilogram costs £6·40, what is the cost of 125g?

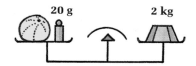

3 What is the weight in kg and g of the melon on the scales?

4 If $\frac{1}{2}$ kg of Coconut Mix costs £2, what is the cost of 750 g?

5 I bought $3\frac{1}{2}$ kg of cherries and $2\frac{3}{4}$ kg of strawberries.
What was the total weight in grams of the fruit I bought?

6 Each of these large books weighs 800 g. What is their
total weight in kilograms?

7 300 g of sultanas cost 60p. How much do 3 kg of sultanas cost?

8 Three-quarters of the chocolates in a box weigh 1 kg 500 g.
What is the weight of all the chocolates?

172

Find the cost of:

1 1ℓ 500 ml at 40p per litre.

2 200 ml at 10p per litre.

3 20 ml at £10 per litre.

4 250 ml at 40p per litre.

5 25 ml at £1 per $\frac{1}{4}$ litre.

6 1ℓ 100 ml at 80p per litre.

7 1750 ml at 40p per litre.

8 390 ml at £10 per litre.

173

1 900 ml of blackcurrant juice was poured into a $1\frac{1}{2}$ litre bottle.
   How many more ml could the bottle hold?

2 How many 25 ml glasses can be filled from $\frac{1}{4}$ litre?

3 How many 350 ml bottles can be filled from $3\frac{1}{2}$ litres?

4 Uzuma made a birthday punch by mixing 900 ml of grapefruit juice,
   900 ml of pineapple juice and $\frac{1}{4}$ ℓ of lemonade.
   How much punch in ℓ and ml did she make?

5 Each tin holds 750 ml of oil. What is the quantity of oil in the
   whole box?

6 450 ml of milk was used from a carton holding $\frac{1}{2}$ ℓ.
   What quantity of milk remained?

7 2 ℓ 400 ml of lemonade was shared equally by 6 boys.
   How many ml did each get?

8 If I filled four 750 ml bottles from this jar of ginger ale,
   how much would be left in the jar?

174

Look at the watch on the right.
In how many minutes will it be:

1 quarter past five?

2 5.43 pm?

3 five minutes past seven in the evening?

4 If this watch is 35 minutes fast, what is the correct time?
   Use the 24-hour clock system.

5 How many minutes is it since breakfast at half past seven?

6 How many hours and minutes is it until noon?

7 If this clock is 40 minutes slow, what is the correct time?

8 If the clock is 40 minutes fast, what is the correct time?